Civil engineering specification for the water industry

(FOURTH EDITION)

Civil engineering
specification
for the
water industry
(FOURTH EDITION)

Published by WRc (1993) plc,
Henley Road
Medmenham
PO Box 16
Marlow
Bucks
SL7 2HD

on behalf of the Water Services Association
1 Queens Anne's Gate
London
SW1H 9BT

ISBN 0 902156 91 8

FOREWORD - FOURTH EDITION

The Civil Engineering Specification for the Water Industry (CESWI) was first published in July 1978, followed by second and third editions in August 1984 and May 1989 respectively. It is the standard document for civil engineering contracts let by the water undertakers and sewerage undertakers in England and Wales, and by bodies such as district councils discharging sewerage functions on their behalf.

In 1992 it was decided to initiate a national survey to elicit comments on how the Third Edition of the Specification might be improved. Announcements were subsequently made in appropriate publications and comments were invited from within the water industry.

The principal changes reflect the transfer of water supply and sewerage functions to water service companies and the coming into force of the New Roads and Street Works Act 1991, together with its associated Regulations and Codes of Practice. Also, following the lead set by the Third Edition of the Civil Engineering Standard Method of Measurement, the section on sewer renovation has been extended to cover water main renovation and ancillary works. Clauses relating to steel pipelines, omitted since the First Edition, have been re-introduced.

Advisory Notes 1 and 2 to the Third Edition of CESWI dealt respectively with the advent of the Construction Products Directive (89/106/EEC) and the Sixth Edition of the ICE Conditions of Contract. The advice in both of them has been followed in the preparation of this Fourth Edition and further guidance has been included on the post-1992 contractual scene within the European Community.

As with previous editions it is envisaged that it will often be necessary to include additional clauses to provide for individual features and the need for such clauses has again been allowed for in the system of numbering. The system should be followed when numbering any additional clauses in order to maintain consistency of presentation.

Contracts for water and sewerage schemes in Scotland and Northern Ireland are let using a standard specification issued by the Scottish Association of Directors of Water and Sewerage Services (SADWSS) and the Department of the Environment for Northern Ireland. The CESWI Working Group had the benefit of observers from the SADWSS Working Party during the preparation of this Fourth Edition.

The Specification was reviewed and redrafted by the following Working Group:

H White	Yorkshire Water (Chairman to 31 March 1993)
B E Spark	Anglian Water (Chairman from 1 April 1993)
C E Tregoing	WRc (Technical Secretary)
T M Allan	Dynamco Ltd
	(representing the Water Companies Association)
D C Bradley	Yorkshire Water
R J Burden	South West Water
K Foulger	Wessex Water
P G Homersham	Thames Water
M B Joyner	Anglian Water (from 1 April 1993)
S Marques	North West Water
P D Mitchell	Severn Trent Water
E Neild	Northumbrian Water
A D Rogerson	Southern Water
P A Scoble	Welsh Water

The following observers represented the SADWSS Working Party:

J McMillen	DoE Northern Ireland - Water Executive
T H Stuart	Tayside Regional Council

The Working Group had the benefit of advice from Mr A F Parsons, Consultant Legal Advisor to WSA, in connection with the New Roads and Street Works Act 1991 and statutory references generally.

CONTENTS

PRODUCT SPECIFICATIONS AND LEVELS OF ATTESTATION

1. Wherever there is an appropriate British Standard or equivalent, or Water Industry specification (WIs), the Specification demands that materials and products should comply with its relevant provisions; it is also preferred that they are Kitemarked where such products are available, though the mark of conformity of any other third party certification body accredited by the National Accreditation Council for Certification Bodies, or any equivalent mark, are acceptable alternatives to this requirement. This approach is consistent with the long-established policy of the water industry, whereby it seeks to improve those Standards with which it is concerned, rather than specifying additional or amended requirements, and gives its full support to BSI or equivalent certification schemes (see Note 3 below). Water industry representation at BSI is co-ordinated by the water industry's Engineering and Operations Committee.

2. Under the provisions of the Construction Products Directive (89/106/EEC) the European Commission decides the appropriate level of attestation when a harmonised European Specification is published under a mandate given in connection with that Directive. The Specification, therefore, now provides for levels of attestation less stringent than full third party certification, where so decided by the Commission. Such relaxation (if any) applies only to the mandated content of harmonised European Standards.

3. A British Standard will not normally be available in the case of newly-developed products, but this is not to be seen as inhibiting the use of such products. Water Industry specifications issued by the Engineering and Operations Committee, deal with products such as these and are called up in the Specification. However, in the case of any innovatory product for which no British Standard or Water Industry specification (or the equivalent of either) exists, preference should be given to products which have been assessed by a third party approvals body as being fit for their intended purpose. Typical UK-based organisations offering such services are the Water Industry Certification Scheme (WICS) and the British Board of Agrément (BBA). The former works closely with the water industry in developing specifications for new products and the latter is authorised to issue European Technical Approvals under the provisions of the Construction Products Directive.

4. In reference to BS codes of practice, a distinction has been drawn between those which comprise, in the main, standards of good workmanship practice - these are called up in the main text of the Specification - and those which deal largely with matters such as temporary works which are the contractor's responsibility under Clause 8 of the Sixth Edition, which are referred to in the Notes for Guidance.

5. The water industry has agreed with BSI Quality Assurance that its representatives will bring to the attention of the Head of Technical Service any problems or complaints experienced with Kitemark certified products. Similarly in respect of products required to comply with a Water Industry specification, any problem or complaint should be brought to the attention of the Chief Executive of WICS. The manager of any other appropriate certification body should be approached in respect of any complaint relative to a product supplied to an equivalent specification. A sample of the questionnaire to be used is given in Appendix XI. A copy of each completed questionnaire should be sent to the head office of the relevant water undertaker or sewerage undertaker marked for the attention of its BSI Standards Liaison Officer. This procedure is not intended to affect the provisions of the Contract.

GENERAL NOTES

1. The following principles have been followed in drafting the original and successive editions of the Specification:

   (i) The Specification is written primarily in terms of the performance required, leaving the Contractor, so far as possible, free to decide his method of working.

   (ii) The document is intended for use with the Sixth Edition of the ICE Conditions of Contract and so, in accordance with Clause 5 of those Conditions, provisions already covered by them are excluded from the Specification. For example, such phrases as 'to the satisfaction (or approval) of the Engineer' have been omitted, being covered by Clause 13(1) of the Sixth Edition.

   (iii) The Specification is intended for use in conjunction with the Third Edition of the Civil Engineering Standard Method of Measurement (CESMM) and the order of subjects follows the same sequence as closely as the scope of the two documents allows.

   (iv) There is no reference in the Specification either to the method of assessing payment or to whether the Employer or the Contractor should bear specific costs; these matters are left for inclusion in the Bill of Quantities and its Preamble.

   (v) References to Acts of Parliament and Statutory Instruments are omitted from the main text (though not from the Notes for Guidance and Associated Topics), since the Contractor's compliance with them is a requirement of Clause 26(3) of the Sixth Edition.

   (vi) Traditional requirements which are desirable but impossible to achieve in a literal sense have been omitted (e.g. 'pipes to be laid true to line and level').

2. Notes for Guidance are printed in the margins beside the text to which they refer and are designed primarily to assist those preparing contract documents. One of their main purposes is to explain apparent omissions from the text such as those referred to in Note 1 above and to cross refer to other documents (Sixth Edition etc.) where such matters are covered.

3. The 'Associated Topics' listed after Sections 1, 3, 6 and 7 serve the same general purpose as the Notes for Guidance and differ from them only in that they do not relate directly to the printed clauses. In most cases they help to explain why such clauses were omitted.

4. Acts of Parliament, Statutory Instruments and other documents quoted in the marginal Notes for Guidance and the accompanying 'Associated Topics' are those in force at the time of publication.

5. Reference to Clause numbers in the main text and in the marginal Notes for Guidance relate to Clause numbers of this Specification.

Feedback Arrangements

Any suggestion for amendment of the Specification should be sent to the Water Services Association, 1 Queen Anne's Gate, London SW1H 9BT.

Technical queries should be referred to the Technical Secretary-CESWI, WRc, Frankland Road, Blagrove, Swindon, Wiltshire, SN5 8YF. Tel: 0793 511711, Fax: 0793 511712

Any clauses in this Specification which relate to work or materials not required by the Works shall be deemed not to apply.

The General Notes, clause headings, marginal Notes for Guidance and the accompanying 'Associated Topics' are not part of the Specification, and are not to affect the interpretation either of the Specification or of the other Contract documents.

SECTION 1

GENERAL

1.1 ENTRY ONTO THE SITE

(i) The Contract should prescribe the extent of the Site, including working areas, accesses and the periods for which they will be available. Reference should be made to any known hazards.

(ii) The Employer may have to obtain planning permission where an access from a classified road is specified. See Clause 26(3)(c) of the Sixth Edition.

(iii) It is assumed that formal entry Notices will have already been served by the Employer and that the Engineer will alert owners and occupiers to impending entry.

(iv) Where appropriate, copies of the Code approved under Section 182 should be made available to tenderers.

1. Prior to the commencement of operations, the Engineer shall supply to the Contractor the names and addresses of relevant owners and occupiers. The Contractor shall notify the Engineer in writing 14 days in advance of his intention to start work within each area of ownership or occupation.

2. The Contractor shall keep records of the dates of his entry onto and departure from all property and lands of each owner and occupier, together with the dates of the erection and removal of all enclosures, and shall furnish copies of these records when required by the Engineer. He shall keep, and furnish, copies of similar records in respect of roads, footpaths and thoroughfares.

3. The Contractor shall at all times comply with the relevant paragraphs of the appropriate 'Code of Practice for the Exercise of Works Powers on Land' approved under Section 182 of the Water Industry Act 1991.

1.2 SURVEY OF HIGHWAYS, PROPERTIES, LANDS AND CROPS

1. Where appropriate, the Engineer shall arrange for surveys to be carried out, in conjunction with the Contractor and the Highway Authority, owners or occupiers, of the condition of highways, properties, lands and crops which may be affected by the Works.

2. Before any work affecting such highways, properties, lands or crops is commenced, the Contractor shall confirm in writing to the Engineer that the relevant survey is a true and accurate record of their condition.

1.3 SITE FENCING

(i) For the Contractor's general responsibility for site fencing, see Clause 19(1) of the Sixth Edition.

1. Where the type and locations of temporary site fencing are described in the Contract, The Contractor shall erect such fencing as soon as he is given possession of the relevant portion of the Site. The Contractor shall regularly inspect and maintain all such fencing, any defects being made good without delay. Access shall be provided in temporary site fencing as necessary for the use of the occupiers of adjacent lands. Temporary site fencing shall remain in position until either it is replaced by permanent fencing or the Works are sufficiently completed to enable that portion of the Site to be brought into use.

1.4 LEVELS AND REFERENCE POINTS

(i) The Contract should prescribe the datum level for the Works, together with any master bench marks. Precise reference of the Works to existing features, or to the Ordnance Survey National Grid, should be shown.

1. The Contractor shall supply to the Engineer details of the value and location of the temporary bench marks and reference points which he proposes to use.

2. The Contractor shall satisfy himself that the existing ground levels as indicated in the Contract are correct. Should the Contractor wish to dispute any levels he shall submit to the Engineer a schedule of the position of the levels considered to be in error and a set of revised levels. The existing ground relevant to the disputed levels shall not be disturbed before the Engineer's decision as to the correct levels is given.

(i) Accommodation descriptions should include any car parking facilities required for the Engineer.

(ii) Any planning permission required for accommodations described in the Contract must be obtained by the Employer. See Clause 26(3)(c) of the Sixth Edition.

(iii) BS 6767: Part 1 deals with transportable accommodation units.

(iv) For the removal of accommodations, see Clause 33 of the Sixth Edition.

(v) If required, insurance of office contents should be a Special Condition of Contract.

1.5 ACCOMMODATION FOR THE ENGINEER

1. The Contractor shall provide, heat, light, clean and maintain, until the completion of the Works, accommodation as described in the Contract for the sole use of the Engineer. Offices and other accommodation shall be erected, furnished, equipped and ready for occupation and use within 7 days of the Works Commencement Date, and fully serviced within 28 days of that Date.

2. Where movable offices are required by the Contract, these shall be relocated from time to time as directed by the Engineer.

3. Where the Contract requires telephone facilities for the Engineer, such facilities shall have separate connection direct to a public telephone exchange with privacy of conversation for the Engineer.

(i) Consent of the Local Planning Authority may be required for billposting or advertising.

1.6 BILLPOSTING AND ADVERTISING

1. The Contractor shall not undertake or allow billposting or advertising of any kind upon the Works without the written consent of the Engineer.

(i) Clause 42(4) of the Sixth Edition deals with the provision by the Contractor of any additional land or interests which he may require for the purposes of the Works.

(ii) The Contract should describe any special precautions necessary to comply with the Employer's obligations under Sections 3, 4 and 5 of the Water Industry Act 1991 (environmental duties)

1.7 INTERFERENCE WITH LAND INTERESTS

1. The Contractor shall confine his constructional operations within the Site, or such other areas of land as may be negotiated, and shall instruct his employees not to trespass.

2. Subject to any unavoidable disturbance which may be necessitated by the execution of the Contract, the Contractor shall not interfere with any sporting, fishing or other rights which may be enjoyed on or near the Site.

3. Before exercising any right negotiated by him in connection with wayleaves or accommodation outside the Site, the Contractor shall notify the Engineer in writing of such arrangements.

(i) For requirements that the Contractor shall not interfere unnecessarily with access, see Clause 29(1) of the Sixth Edition.

1.8 INTERFERENCE WITH ACCESS TO PROPERTIES AND APPARATUS

1. Before interfering with access to any property, the Contractor shall provide alternative arrangements. The Contractor shall notify the Engineer and the relevant occupiers in writing 14 days in advance of any such interference and shall confirm to the Engineer that alternative arrangements have been agreed.

2. The Contractor shall not obstruct access to any manhole or other surface cover.

(i) This Clause will assist in the operation of Clause 22 of the Sixth Edition by ensuring that all parties are aware of any difficulties which may have arisen during the Contract.

1.9 PROCEDURE FOR COMPLAINTS AND CLAIMS FOR DAMAGE

1. Details of all claims or warnings of intended claims which the Contractor may receive in respect of matters against which he is required by the Contract to indemnify the Employer shall be notified without delay to the Engineer, who shall likewise pass to the Contractor any such claims or warnings which may be submitted directly to the Engineer or Employer.

2. A similar exchange of information shall also be made in relation to all complaints which may be received.

3. The Contractor shall notify the Engineer in writing immediately following any damage or injury arising out of the execution of the Works.

1.10   PROTECTION AGAINST DAMAGE

1. The Contractor shall take all necessary precautions to avoid causing any unwarranted damage to roads, lands, properties, trees and other features and, during the currency of the Contract, shall deal promptly with any complaints by owners or occupiers.

2. Where any portion of the Works is close to, across, or under any existing apparatus of Statutory Undertakers, the Highway Authority or other parties, the Contractor shall temporarily support and work round, under or adjacent to all apparatus in a manner designed to avoid damage, leakage or danger, and to ensure uninterrupted operation.

3. Should any leakages or damage be discovered, the Contractor shall at once notify the Engineer and the Statutory Undertaker, Highway Authority or owner concerned, as appropriate and the Contractor shall afford every facility for the repair or replacement of the apparatus affected.

(i) This Clause refers to the avoidance of damage. See Clause 22(1) of the Sixth Edition for liabilities following the occurrence of any damage.

(ii) For the avoidance and consequences of damage to highways by 'extraordinary traffic', see Clause 30 of the Sixth Edition.

(iii) The Bill of Quantities should be so prepared that Tenderers may price for working round and temporarily supporting apparatus. Any permanent support known to be required should be described in the Contract.

1.11   APPARATUS OF STATUTORY UNDERTAKERS, HIGHWAY AUTHORITIES AND OTHERS

1. The Contract indicates what are believed to be the positions of the apparatus of Statutory Undertakers, Highway Authorities and others close to the Works, but no warranty is given as to the accuracy or completeness of this information.

2. The accepted programme of Works shall show information necessary to enable the Engineer to arrange for all diversions, or removals, of apparatus described in the Contract to be carried out at the appropriate time.

3. The Contractor shall liaise with all relevant Statutory Undertakers, the Highway Authorities and other owners of apparatus before commencing any excavations, and shall satisfy himself as to the exact position of existing apparatus which may affect or be affected by the construction of the Works.

4. The Contractor shall notify the Engineer in advance of any diversion or removal of apparatus which he may require for his own convenience or because of his proposed method of working and shall comply with any requirements of the Engineer with respect to them.

5. Should any apparatus be found to exist which is not indicated, or not as indicated, in the Contract, the Contractor shall at once give written notification to the Engineer.

(i) The Contract should describe any apparatus which requires diverting or removing on account of its interference with the construction of the Permanent Works.

(ii) The Water Services Association, the Water Companies Association, and British Gas have agreed a 'Model Consultative Procedure for Pipeline Construction Involving Deep Excavation', which was published in January 1993.

(iii) The information given under Clause 1.11.1 would not normally include connections to and from premises and street furniture.

(iv) The diversion or removal of apparatus will normally be undertaken by agreement between the appropriate Statutory Undertaker and the Employer.

(v) Any requirements of Statutory Undertakers or public bodies should be described in the Contract.

(vi) For works likely to affect other apparatus in a street see Section 69 of the New Roads and Street Works Act 1991.

1.12 TRAFFIC REQUIREMENTS

(i) Chapter 8 covers many aspects which are sometimes found in specifications, such as traffic signals and signs, one-way working and minimum carriageway widths.

(ii) 'Site' includes any tip provided by the Employer for the purposes of the Contract.

(iii) The Contract should include details of any road closures to be arranged by the Employer.

(iv) For general requirements relating to road closures and diversions, see Paragraph 8.53 of Chapter 8.

1. The Contractor shall comply with the Code of Practice 'Safety at Street Works and Road Works' issued by the Secretary of State for Transport under Section 65 of the New Roads and Street Works Act 1991. He shall also comply with the relevant provisions of the Traffic Safety Measures for Road Works, as contained in Chapter 8 of the 'Traffic Signs Manual' published by Her Majesty's Stationery Office, and with the relevant provisions of Advice Notes TD/21/85 'Portable Traffic Signals at Road Works on Single Carriageway Roads', TA/12/81 'Traffic signals on High Speed Roads' and TA/13/81 'Requirements for the Installation of Traffic Signals and Associated Control Equipment' published by the Department of Transport.

2. Before any work in or affecting the use of any highway is commenced, the Contractor's proposed method of working shall be agreed with, and confirmed in writing to, the Engineer and the Highway and Police Authorities.

3. Throughout the execution of the Works and the Defects Correction Period, the Contractor shall co-operate with the Highway and Police Authorities concerning works in, or access to, the highway. The Contractor shall inform the Engineer of any requirements of, or arrangements made with, the Highway and Police Authorities.

4. Where the diversion of any existing carriageway, footway or public right of way is temporarily necessitated by the Works, the Contractor shall provide and maintain an alternative which shall be operational before interference with the existing way.

5. Where ramps are required, they shall be provided and maintained to a standard suitable in all respects for the class or classes of traffic or pedestrians requiring to use them.

6. The Contractor shall take all reasonable steps to prevent vehicles entering and leaving the Site depositing mud or other debris on the surface of adjacent roads or footways, and shall remove expeditiously any materials so deposited.

1.13 TIDINESS OF SITE

(i) See also Clauses 13(1) and 19(1) of the Sixth Edition.

1. The Contractor shall be responsible for the proper upkeep and maintenance of the Site and the Works and shall remove from the Site rubbish and other waste as it accumulates. Materials and equipment shall be positioned, stored and stacked in an orderly manner.

1.14 WORKS AFFECTING WATERCOURSES

(i) It is assumed that all necessary Statutory consents relating to the Permanent Works will have been obtained by the Employer.

(ii) Any requirement for the Contractor to liaise with the appropriate Land Drainage Authority should be described in the Contract.

(iii) The following Statutory provisions are also relevant:

1. Impeding flow in a watercourse: Water Resources Act 1991, Section 107 and Land Drainage Act 1991, Section 25.

1. The Contractor shall notify the Engineer in writing 14 days in advance of his intention to start any part of the Works affecting a watercourse, canal or lake.

2. The Contractor shall be responsible for maintaining watercourses within the Site in effective working condition at all times.

3. The Contractor shall take all practicable measures, which shall be to the prior approval of the Engineer, to prevent the deposition of silt or other material in, and the pollution of, any existing watercourse, canal, lake, reservoir, borehole, aquifer or catchment area, arising from his operations.

2. Pollution of a watercourse or underground strata: Water Resources Act 1991, Sections 85, 86 and 90, Salmon & Fresh Water Fisheries Act, 1975, Section 4.

(i) The term 'restricted operations' is defined in Paragraph 1.4 of 'Operational Guidelines for the Protection of Drinking Water Supplies'.

(ii) Provision should be made in the Bill of Quantities for all medical testing required by this Clause.

(iii) The use of the term 'pathogenic organism test' has been avoided, since other tests will be involved.

1.15 CONTAMINATION OF WATER SUPPLIES

1. Before any person is engaged on work described in the Contract as involving 'restricted operations', he shall be notified of the need for personal hygiene and the dangers of contamination, shall complete a medical questionnaire provided by the Employer and, where there is a need, shall be tested to indicate that he is not a carrier of typhoid or other waterborne disease. The Contractor shall notify the Engineer of any person who has been certified by a doctor as suffering from an illness associated with looseness of the bowels, and no such person shall be employed on such work until the Employer's medical adviser is satisfied that it is safe for him to be so employed.

2. The Contractor shall comply with the relevant provisions of 'Operational Guidelines for the Protection of Drinking Water Supplies' published by the Water Authorities Association.

(i) Section 4 of 'Safe Working in Sewers and at Sewage Works' refers to the water industry guidelines for the use of respiratory protective equipment. Those guidelines should also be incorporated in any other type of contract where the use of breathing apparatus will be required.

1.16 SAFETY IN SEWERS AND AT SEWAGE WORKS

1. Where the Contract requires work to be carried out within or adjacent to any sewer or at a sewage works, the Contractor shall comply with the relevant provisions of 'Safe Working in Sewers and at Sewage Works', published by the National Joint Health and Safety Committee for the Water Service.

(i) See also The Work in Compressed Air Special Regulations 1958 as amended.

(ii) The CIRIA Code R44 gives recommendations as to standards of good practice for work in compressed air.

1.17 WORK IN COMPRESSED AIR

1. Where work is to be carried out in compressed air, the Contractor shall apply to the Chief Inspector of Factories for a Certificate of Approval to the use of the decompression tables incorporated in the 'Medical Code of Practice for Work in Compressed Air (Third Edition) 1982, reprinted with amendments 1992' (CIRIA Report R44), published by the Construction Industry Research and Information Association. The Contractor shall comply with all other relevant provisions of the above Code.

(i) See also Clauses 8(3) and 19(1) of the Sixth Edition.

1.18 EMERGENCY ARRANGEMENTS

1. The Contractor shall maintain arrangements whereby he can quickly call out labour outside normal working hours to carry out any work needed for an emergency associated with the Works. The Engineer shall be provided at all times with a list of addresses and telephone numbers of the Contractor's staff who are currently responsible for organising emergency work.

2. The Contractor shall acquaint himself and his employees with any relevant local arrangements which are in existence for dealing with emergencies.

(i) The following Statutory and other provisions are also relevant:

1. Storage and Use of Explosives: Construction (General Provisions) Regulations 1961, Part VI. Explosives Acts 1875 and 1923 and Orders in Council Nos. 6, 6A, and 6C, made under the 1875 Act.

Control of Explosives Regulations 1991.

2. Storage of Petroleum: Petroleum Spirit (Motor Vehicles etc.) Regulations 1929 Petroleum (Consolidation) Act 1928

3. Storage of Highly Flammable Substances: Highly Flammable Liquids and Liquefied Petroleum Gases Regulations 1972.

1.19 EXPLOSIVES AND DANGEROUS SUBSTANCES

1. No explosive or other dangerous substance shall be brought onto the Site or used for any purpose unless the Contractor has previously obtained the written approval of the Engineer.

2. The location of each explosives magazine and store of any other dangerous substance on the Site shall be approved in writing by the Engineer.

3. The storage of blasting explosives shall be in accordance with the conditions (if any) of the statutory licence obtained by the Contractor and the relevant provisions of BS 5607.

(i) All public electricity suppliers require compliance with the I.E.E. Wiring Regulations where mains electricity is to be used. This Clause ensures that the same provisions apply in the case of any on-site generation.

(ii) The provisions of the I.E.E. Wiring Regulations embrace BS 4363 Distribution Units for Electricity Supplies for Construction and Building Sites and BS 7375 Distribution of Electricity on Construction and Building Sites.

1.20 ELECTRICITY DISTRIBUTION ON THE SITE

1. All electrical installations forming part of the Temporary Works shall comply with the relevant provisions of the 'Regulations for Electrical Installations' (I.E.E. Wiring Regulations - 16th Edition), published by the Institution of Electrical Engineers.

(i) The period of 42 days is consistent with that used for defining the 'Base Index Figure' in sub-clause (2)(b) of the Contract Price Fluctuations clause for use in connection with the Sixth Edition.

1.21 BRITISH STANDARDS AND OTHER DOCUMENTS

1. British Standards and other documents referred to in the Contract shall be deemed to be those current 42 days prior to the date for return of Tenders.

2. Any reference in the Contract to a Standard published by the British Standards Institution, or to the specification of another body, shall be construed equally as reference to an equivalent one.

ASSOCIATED TOPICS

The following topics are dealt with by statute or by the Sixth Edition of the ICE Conditions of Contract and are therefore excluded from the Specification:

1. NOISE:

Clauses 29(2)(3) and (4) of the Sixth Edition deals with the subject generally, but special clauses may be necessary depending on particular circumstances. The provisions of Part III of the Control of Pollution Act 1974 and the Health and Safety at Work etc. Act 1974 will apply. The Control of Noise (Codes of Practice for Construction and Open Sites) Order 1984 gave approval to the use of BS 5228: Parts 1 and 2 in relation to the control of construction noise.

2. CARE AND PROTECTION OF THE WORKS:

See Clauses 20(1) and 39(1) of the Sixth Edition.

3. ILLUMINATION OF WORKS:

See Regulation 47 of the Construction (General Provisions) Regulations 1961 as amended by the Construction (Metrication) Regulations 1984

4. SAFETY AT STREET WORKS

See Clause 19(1) of the Sixth Edition, the Code of Practice 'Safety at Street Works and Road Works' under Section 65 of the New Roads and Street Works Act 1991 and Section 66(1) of that Act (Avoidance of unnecessary delay or obstruction).

5. FIRST AID:

See the Health and Safety (First-Aid) Regulations 1981 and the approved Code of Practice issued in relation to the Regulations giving guidance as to their requirements.

6. SITE ROADS:

See Clause 8(1) of the Sixth Edition.

7. ACCESS LADDERS, PLATFORMS ETC:

See the Construction (Working Places) Regulations 1966 as amended by the Construction (Metrication) Regulations 1984.

8. WELFARE FACILITIES:

See the Construction (Health and Welfare) Regulations 1966 as amended by the Construction (Health and Welfare) (Amended) Regulations 1974, and section 7 of the Factories Act 1961.

9. SITE INVESTIGATION:

See the following:

(i) Clause 11(1) and (2) of the Sixth Edition.

(ii) BS 5930 and CIRIA Special Publication 25 - 'Site investigation manual'.

10. CONTRACTORS' SITE ACCOMMODATION:

(i) For the provision and adequacy of the Contractor's accommodations see Clauses 8(1) and 11(2) of the Sixth Edition.

(ii) For the Contractor's responsibilities for obtaining any planning permissions which may be required in respect of his accommodations see Clause 26(3) of the Sixth Edition.

11. CONFIDENTIALITY:

Any requirement for the Contractor to treat the Contract or any part of it as private and confidential should be a Special Condition of Contract and not a Specification clause.

12. FIRE PRECAUTIONS IN SITE ACCOMMODATION:

For requirements as to fire certificates for site accommodation, see Paragraph 15 of Part 1 of Schedule 1 to the Fire Certificates (Special Premises) Regulations 1976.

13. NUISANCE:

See Clause 29 of the Sixth Edition and section 92 of the Public Health Act 1936.

14. DEALING WITH FLOWS IN SEWERS:

See Clauses 8(1) and 14(6) of the Sixth Edition. Estimates of dry-weather and peak flows should be indicated in the Contract.

15. WATER INDUSTRY'S DUTY TO CONTRACTORS:

See 'The Water Industry's Duty under the Health and Safety at Work etc. Act to Contractors Employed by the Industry', published by the National Joint Health and Safety Committee for the Water Service - Employers guideline No. 2.

SECTION 2

MATERIALS

2.1 STANDARDS AND SUBMISSION OF MATERIALS

(i) Where appropriate, additional quality control of materials should be carried out at manufacturers' or suppliers' premises.

(ii) In January 1989 the WAA Sewers and Water Mains Committee announced that all specifications produced in its Information and Guidance Note series were to be known henceforth as Water Industry specifications (WIs). The numbering system remains unchanged.

(iii) For the Engineer's right of access to suppliers' premises, see Clause 37 of the Sixth Edition.

(iv) For the terms under which samples are to be supplied, see Clause 36(2) of the Sixth Edition. For testing, see Additional description rule A3 to Class 'A' of the CESMM.

(v) Before accepting any material which will come into contact with potable water, or water to be used for potable supply, the Engineer shall have regard to the provisions of Regulation 25 of the Water Supply (Water Quality) Regulations 1989. Reference should be made to the current list of approved substances prepared by the Committee on Chemicals and Materials of Construction for Use in Public Water Supply and Swimming Pools, issued by the Department of the Environment. Reference should also be made to the current issue of the 'Water Fittings and Materials Directory', published by WRc. Where appropriate, copies should be made available to Tenderers.

(vi) Requirements for the testing of materials for use in contact with potable water are dealt with in:
Metallic - British Standard DD 201
Non-metallic - BS 6920 and IGN No. 5-01-02.

1. Wherever, in respect of any British Standard (BS), a BSI Kitemark Certification Scheme is available, all materials required to comply with that Standard, or the containers of such materials, shall be marked with the BSI Certification Trade Mark (the Kitemark). The mark of conformity of any other third party certification body accredited by the National Accreditation Council for Certification Bodies or an equivalent mark shall be an acceptable alternative to this requirement.

2. Wherever, in respect of any Water Industry specification (WIs) published by the UK Water Industry Engineering and Operations Committee or its predecessor, a Water Industry Certification Scheme or equivalent is available, all materials required to comply with that specification, or the containers of such materials, shall be marked with the Water Industry Certification Mark (the Watermark) or the mark of conformity of the equivalent scheme.

3. Where a technical specification has been established under the provisions of Directive 89/106/EEC, the relevant system of conformity attestation chosen by the Commission of the European Communities shall apply to those elements of that specification which relate to a mandate given by the Commission and sub-clauses 1 and 2 above shall only apply as appropriate. However, this sub-clause shall not apply where the Contract under the provisions of another Directive defines such further quality assurance requirements as are necessary to complement any technical specification.

4. The requirements of sub-clauses 1 and 2 above shall not apply where the Engineer is satisfied and confirms to the Contractor in writing that third party quality assured materials are not readily available or appropriate. In such a case, and where materials are required to comply with other British Standards, specifications or their equivalents, the Contractor shall submit to the Engineer test certificates, furnished by the supplier or manufacturer of the materials, indicating compliance with the relevant specification.

5. As soon as possible after the Contract has been awarded, the Contractor shall submit to the Engineer for his approval a list of his proposed suppliers and sources of materials required for the execution of the Works.

6. Samples shall be taken in accordance with the appropriate British Standard where applicable.

7. The materials subsequently supplied shall conform to the quality of samples which have been approved by the Engineer.

8. Names of additional suppliers and sources may be submitted by the Contractor during the execution of the Contract, but no source of supply shall be changed without the Engineer's approval.

(vii) Directive 89/106/EEC is the Construction Products Directive and an example of 'another Directive' would be 90/531/EEC: The 'Utilities Directive'.

2.2 STORAGE OF MATERIALS

1. Materials and components shall be stored in such a manner as to preserve their quality and condition to the standards required by the Contract.

2. The quantity of materials and components stored on the Site shall be consistent with that necessary for efficient working.

2.3 HANDLING AND USE OF MATERIALS

(i) An understanding of manufacturers' recommendations is necessary before their applicability can be assessed.

1. Materials and components shall be handled in such a manner as to avoid any damage or contamination, and in accordance with all applicable recommendations of the manufacturers.

2. Unless otherwise described in the Contract, the use, installation, application or fixing of materials and components shall be in accordance with all applicable recommendations of the manufacturers. Where appropriate, the Contractor shall make use of any technical advisory services offered by manufacturers.

2.4 IMPORTED TOPSOIL

(i) For the definition of in-situ topsoil, see Clause 3.3.

1. Imported topsoil shall comply with BS 3882 and be of light or medium texture, having a pH value of between 6.0 and 7.5. Imported topsoil shall not contain stones greater than 50 mm in size, nor have a total stone content exceeding 10% by mass.

2.5 IMPORTED TURF

(i) For in-situ turf for relaying, see Clauses 3.2 and 3.10.

(ii) Clause 3 of BS 3969 permits up to 50% of Dwarf Leafy Perennial Ryegrass unless otherwise specified.

1. Imported turf shall comply with BS 3969 and be delivered to the Site within 36 hours of lifting. Constituent grasses and their proportions shall comply with the provisions of Clause 3 of BS 3969.

2. Turves shall be 300 mm wide and of uniform thickness not less than 40 mm, in lengths not exceeding 1 m. Turves shall not be lifted in frosty weather.

2.6 GRASS SEED

(i) The four mixtures given are available nationally, examples of their individual application being as follows:

1. Grass seed shall be a tested blend of named varieties and certificates of purity and germination shall be provided. The blend shall consist of one of the following mixtures:

Mixture	Application
1	General application which will give satisfactory germination on a wide variety of soils.
2	Heavy soils and wet areas.
3	Drier, less fertile soils.
4	Soils with very low fertility, low pH or sandy soils.

Variety	Percentage by mass			
	Mixture 1	Mixture 2	Mixture 3	Mixture 4
Dwarf Leafy Perennial Ryegrass	20-30	-	-	-
Smooth-stalked Meadow Grass	25-35	-	20-30	0-15
Rough-stalked Meadow Grass	-	15-25	-	-
Creeping Red Fescue	30-40	40-50	35-45	20-50
Fine Leaved Sheep's Fescue	-	-	10-20	10-40
Chewings Fescue	-	-	-	10-40
Browntop Bent	5-15	5-15	5-15	0-10
Crested Dogstail	-	-	5-15	-
Timothy	-	20-30	-	-
White Clover	-	-	-	0-10

(ii) All mixtures have been selected to provide slow growing grass with a low maintenance requirement. Mixture 1 will give the most rapid cover after germination, but will require more maintenance than Mixtures 2, 3 and 4.

(iii) The mixtures are not intended for use on agricultural land, where the farmer's requirements should be ascertained.

(iv) The required grass seed mixture should be described in the Contract.

(v) For guidance on the use of grass in hydraulic engineering practice, see CIRIA Technical Note-TN71.

(vi) In view of the requirements of the Wildlife and Countryside Act 1981, consideration should be given where appropriate to the inclusion of an approved wild flower mix with the grass seed.

2.7   FERTILISER

1. Fertilisers shall consist of compounds containing urea nitrogen, phosphoric acid and potash in the proportions by mass, as set out below:

Chemical	General purpose	Pre-seeding	Post-establishment
Urea nitrogen	5%	-	46%
Phosphoric acid	15%	21%	-
Potash	15%	12%	-

(i) The general purpose compound should be used as a single application, prior to seeding, where good root establishment but slow growth is required. The pre-seeding and post-establishment compounds require application both before and after germination respectively and will promote good root establishment, followed by rapid growth.

(ii) The compounds are not intended for use on agricultural land, where the farmer's requirements should be ascertained.

2.8   TREES AND SHRUBS

1. Trees and shrubs shall comply with the relevant provisions of the appropriate British Standard, as set out below:

Type	BS
Ordinary nursery stock	3936: Part 1
Semi-mature trees	4043
Advanced nursery stock	4043

QUALITY ASSURED PRODUCTS PREFERRED — SEE CLAUSE 21

2.9 WATER

1. Water for use with cement, or in contact with potable water mains and installations, shall be obtained from a water undertaker's supply and be of potable quality.

(i) In certain areas, supplementary mains carrying non-potable water have been laid, and the use of this water with cement or in contact with potable water mains and installations has been prohibited.

(ii) Where potable mains water is not available, alternative provisions should be described in the Contract. BS 3148 gives details of tests for water for making concrete.

2.10 AGGREGATES FOR CONCRETE

1. Aggregates for concrete shall comply with the relevant provisions of the appropriate British Standard, as set out below:

(i) Any restrictions on the source, type or group classification of aggregates should be described in the Contract.

(ii) Concrete designed to retain an aqueous liquid should be described as such in the Contract.

(iii) Where there is the likelihood of unacceptable damage from alkali-silica reaction, specific precautions to minimise it should be described in the Contract in accordance with the recommendations of Technical Report No. TR30 'Alkali-silica Reaction - Minimising the Risk of Damage to Concrete' published by the Concrete Society in October 1987 and BRE Digest 330 published by the Building Research Establishment in March 1988. Guidance relating to alkali-silica reaction is contained in Clause 4.2.4 of BS 5328: Part 1.

(iv) For the limitation of total chloride ion content of the concrete mix, see Clause 4.9.2.

(v) The limit for water absorption is consistent with Clause 6.2.2 of BS 8007.

Type of aggregate	Type of concrete	
	Standard and Designated mixes and those designed to retain an aqueous liquid	Designed mixes and Prescribed mixes
Aggregates from natural sources	BS 882	BS 882
Air-cooled blast furnace slag aggregate	BS 1047	BS 1047
Foamed or expanded blastfurnace slag lightweight aggregate	-	BS 3797
Clinker and furnace bottom ash aggregates	-	BS 3797
Lightweight aggregates	-	BS 3797

2. Aggregates complying with BS 3797 or BS 1047 shall have values of 'ten per cent fines', aggregate impact and chloride ion content which are consistent with the relevant provisions of BS 882.

3. The water absorption of aggregates for concrete designed to retain an aqueous liquid shall not exceed 3% when measured in accordance with BS 812: Part 2.

2.11 AGGREGATES FOR HIGH STRENGTH CONCRETE TOPPING

1. Aggregates for high strength concrete topping (granolithic finish) shall comply with BS 882 and be 10 mm nominal size, graded in accordance with Table 6 of that Standard.

(i) The requirement for sands to be washed is additional to the requirements of the Standards, but is in line with the main conclusion of CIRIA Report R59 - 'Building Sands: Availability, Usage and Compliance with Specification Requirements'.

2.12 SANDS

1. Sands for mortar and grout shall comply with BS 1200 and be graded in accordance with Table 1 of that Standard.

2. Sands for floor screeds shall comply with the relevant provisions of BS 882.

3. Sands for external renderings and internal plastering with lime and Portland cement shall comply with the relevant provisions of BS 1199.

4. All sands required to comply with BS 882, BS 1199 or BS 1200 shall be washed sands.

2.13 GROUND GRANULATED BLASTFURNACE SLAG

1. Ground granulated blastfurnace slag (ggbs) for use with Portland cement shall comply with BS 6699.

2.14 PULVERISED-FUEL ASH

1. Pulverised-fuel ash (pfa) for use as a component material in cementitious grout or non-structural concrete shall comply with BS 3892: Part 2, Grade A.

2. Pfa for use as a cementitious component in structural concrete and annulus grouts shall comply with BS 3892: Part 1. Pfa for annulus grouts shall be preblended and bagged before delivery to the Site.

3. Conditioned pfa for use as a fill material shall be supplied with an optimum moisture content and maximum dry density in the ranges 18-25% and 1200-1500 kg/m^3 respectively, when determined in accordance with BS 1377: Part 4 (2.5kg Rammer Method). Water content shall be within ±2% of the optimum moisture content.

2.15 CEMENT

1. Cement shall:

(a) be factory-produced by the cement manufacturer and comply with the provisions of the appropriate British Standard, as set out below:

(i) The permitted type(s) of cement should be described in the Contract.

(ii) The Third Division of Class 'F' of the CESMM requires that the type of cement should be stated in item descriptions for in-situ concrete. The remaining work classifications are not so specific, and, to ensure clarity, the required type of cement should always be stated.

(iii) BS 5224 cement is not a 'permitted cement' under BS 5328: Part 1 nor is it included in BS 8110: Part 1.

(iv) BS 146: permits the 'cement' to contain not more than 65% ggbs by mass.

Cement type	BS
Ordinary Portland	12
Rapid hardening Portland	12
Portland- blast furnace	146
Low-heat Portland	1370
Sulfate-resisting Portland	4027
Low-heat Portland - blastfurnace	4246
Supersulfated	4248
Masonry	5224
Pozzolanic cement with pfa as pozzolana	6610
Portland pfa	6588

or

(b) consist of a normal or special combination of cement complying with the relevant provisions of BS 12 and ggbs or pfa in accordance with the following, to be included as part of the concrete mix by simultaneously combining them with the other concrete materials at the concrete mixer:

(v) Normal combinations of cement facilitate resistance to sulfate attack under exposure classes 1 and 2; special combinations will resist classes 2 and 3. See Table 6.1 of BS 8110: Part 1 and Clause 6.2 of BS 8007. For further guidance see BRE Digest 363.

(vi) Where there is the likelihood of unacceptable damage from alkali-silica reaction, specific precautions to minimise it should be described in the Contract in accordance with the recommendations of Technical Report TR30 'Alkali-silica Reaction - Minimising the Risk of Damage to Concrete' published by the Concrete Society in October 1987 and BRE Digest 330 published by the Building Research Establishment in March 1988. Guidance relating to alkali-silica reaction is contained in Clause 4.2.4. of BS 5328: Part 1.

(vii) Cement for annulus grouts should comply with either BS 12 or BS 4027.

Cementitious component other than cement	Use of concrete	British Standard to be complied with	Percentage by mass of total cementitious content	
			normal	special
pfa	Any	BS 3892: Part 1	15 - 35	25 - 40
ggbs	Concrete designed to retain an aqueous liquid	BS 6699	0 - 50	70 - 90
ggbs	Other	BS 6699	0 - 65	70 - 90

2. For all cement used in structural concrete the Contractor shall provide when requested by the Engineer certificates of the relevant proportions of any ggbs or pfa.

3. White and coloured Portland cement shall comply with the chemical and physical requirements of BS 12. Added pigments shall comply with BS 1014 and shall be mixed with the cement in accordance with the manufacturer's instructions. The amount of added pigments shall not exceed 10% of cement by mass, except for carbon black, where the limit shall be 2%.

4. Blast furnace slag cement for the in-situ lining of water mains shall comply with WIs No. 4-13-01.

(i) Clause 3 of BS 5328: Part 1 prohibits the use of admixtures in standard mixes and restricts their use in designated mixes.

(ii) Clause 2.16.2 is consistent with Clause 6.1.5.4 of BS 8110: Part 1.

2.16 ADMIXTURES FOR CONCRETE OR GROUT

1. Accelerating, retarding and water-reducing admixtures for concrete or grout shall comply with the relevant provisions in BS 5075: Part 1. Air-entraining admixtures shall comply with the relevant provisions of BS 5075: Part 2. Superplasticizing admixtures shall comply with the relevant provisions of BS 5075: Part 3.

2. Calcium chloride shall not be used in concrete which is to be reinforced, contain embedded metal, or has been designed to retain an aqueous liquid. Where used with sulfate-resisting cement, or in concrete which is to be reinforced or contain embedded metal, the chloride ion content of admixtures shall not exceed 2% by mass of the admixture or 0.03% by mass of the cement. Admixtures containing chlorides shall not be used in reinforced concrete designed to retain an aqueous liquid.

(i) Clause 23.2.3 of BS 5628: Part 3 advises that lime used for mortar should be non-hydraulic (high calcium or magnesian) or semi-hydraulic (i.e. lime putty).

2.17 LIME FOR MORTAR

1. Lime for mortar shall be in the form of lime putty, complying with the relevant provisions of BS 890.

(i) The nominal size of medium should be described in the Contract.

2.18 FILTER MEDIA

1. Media from natural sources, or which derives from the reduction of iron ore in a blastfurnace, and for use as medium in biological percolating filters, shall be crushed rock or blastfurnace slag complying with the relevant provisions of BS 1438.

(ii) Appendix E6 of BS 1438 gives recommendations for the placing of filter media.

(iii) An additional specification will be required for a filter medium other than those covered by BS 1438.

(i) The required class of grout, together with the type of cement and any admixture, should be described in the Contract.

2.19 CEMENT GROUTS

1. Cement grout shall be mixed in the relevant proportions indicated in the following table using the minimum quantity of water to ensure the necessary fluidity and to render it capable of penetrating the work.

Class	Nominal mix by mass		
	Cement	Sand	pfa
G1	1	-	-
G2	1	3	-
G3	1	10	-
G4	1	-	10
G5	1	-	4
G6	1	-	½

2. Cement grout shall be used within one hour of mixing, except where containing a retardant admixture.

3. Sulfate-resisting cement shall not be used as a constituent of grouts containing pfa.

(i) Although the CESMM generally requires components of concrete and grout mixes to be measured by mass, there is no corresponding reference to mortars. Volumetric mixes consistent with BS 5628: Part 3, BS 4721 and PD 6472 have, therefore, been specified.

(ii) IGN No. 4-10-01 deals with mortar.

2.20 MORTAR

1. Mortar shall be mixed only as and when required in the relevant proportions indicated in the following table, until its colour and consistency are uniform. The constituent materials shall be accurately gauged, allowance being made for bulking of sand.

Nominal mix by volume					
Class	Cement:lime putty:sand	Cement:sand with plasticizer		Class	Masonry cement: sand
M1	1:0 to ¼:3	1:2½ to 3		M5	1:2 to 2½
M2	1:½:4 to 4½	1:3 to 4		M6	1:2½ to 3½
M3	1:1:5 to 6	1:5 to 6		M7	1:4 to 5
M4	1:2:8 to 9	1:7 to 8		M8	1:5½ to 6½

2. Ready-mixed lime: sand for mortar and ready-to-use retarded mortar shall comply with the relevant provisions of BS 4721.

3. All mortar shall be conveyed fresh to the Works as required for use. Mortar which has begun to set or which has been Site-mixed for a period of more than one hour in the case of classes M1, M2, M5 and M6, and two hours in the case of Classes M3, M4, M7 and M8 shall not be used. Plasticizing and set retarding mortar admixtures shall comply with BS 4887: Parts 1 and 2 respectively and shall be supplied with instructions for use.

2.21 STEEL REINFORCEMENT

(i) The Contract should describe whether Type 1 (square twisted) or Type 2 (ribbed) high yield steel bars are required.

1. Steel reinforcement shall comply with the relevant provisions of the appropriate British Standard, as set out below:

Type	BS
Carbon steel bars	4449
Cold reduced steel wire	4482
Steel fabric	4483

2. Steel fabric reinforcement shall be welded at the intersections and, unless otherwise described in the Contract, shall be delivered to the Site in flat sheets.

2.22 TYING WIRE

1. Tying wire for steel reinforcement shall be 1.6 mm diameter finally annealed mild steel wire, complying with BS 1052.

2.23 COVER BLOCKS AND SPACERS FOR REINFORCEMENT

1. Cover blocks and spacers shall be designed to maintain the correct clear cover of concrete over steel reinforcement, shall be as small as possible consistent with their purpose, and of a shape acceptable to the Engineer.

2. Concrete cover blocks shall be manufactured with a 10 mm maximum aggregate size and otherwise produced to the same specification as the surrounding concrete. Wire cast in the block for the purpose of tying it to the reinforcement shall comply with Clause 2.22.

3. Spacers shall be of rust-proof material and shall not produce staining, or otherwise be detrimental to the concrete or steel.

2.24 PRECAST CONCRETE PRODUCTS

1. Constituent materials of precast concrete products shall comply with the relevant requirements of this Specification, except where an appropriate British Standard includes specified requirements to the contrary.

2. Except where otherwise specified in a relevant British Standard or described in the Contract, the surface finish of precast concrete products shall be Rough Finish for surfaces next to earth and elsewhere Fair Finish.

2.25 WATERPROOF PAPER

1. Waterproof paper shall be Grade 'BIF' complying with the relevant provisions of BS 1521.

2.26 PLASTIC SHEETING AND SLEEVING

(i) A film thickness of 125 μm is equivalent to 500 gauge.

(ii) The colour specifications and amended requirements for layflat widths are consistent with the recommendations of IGN No. 4-50-01.

1. Plastic sheeting for waterproof underlay shall be free from tears and voids and be substantially free from pinholes and other discontinuities. It shall have a composition in accordance with Clause 3 of BS 6076 and a nominal film thickness of 125 μm.

2. Tubular polyethylene film for use as a loose protective sleeving for buried iron pipes and fittings shall comply with the relevant provisions of BS 6076, except that the nominal layflat width shall be 280 mm for use with 80 mm and 100 mm nominal internal diameter pipelines incorporating push-in flexible joints, and 400 mm for 150 mm nominal internal diameter pipelines. Sleeving for pipes for below ground use for potable water shall be coloured blue and all other sleeving black.

(iii) IGN No. 4-50-02 gives operational guidelines for the transportation, handling and laying of ductile iron pipes with factory applied polyethylene sleeving.

2.27 VITRIFIED CLAY PIPES AND PIPELINE FITTINGS

1. Vitrified clay pipes and pipeline fittings shall comply with the relevant provisions of BS EN 295 or BS 65 for surface water type pipes with flexible mechanical joints, unless otherwise described in the Contract.

2. Extra chemically resistant pipes and fittings shall comply with the relevant provisions of BS 65.

(i) IGN No. 4-11-01 deals with vitrified clay pipes and fittings.

(ii) The type of joint and jointing materials for extra chemically resistant pipes should be described in the Contract.

2.28 CONCRETE PIPES AND FITTINGS

1. Unreinforced and reinforced concrete pipes and fittings with flexible or ogee joints shall comply with the relevant provisions of BS 5911: Parts 100 and 110 respectively.

2. All pipes and fittings shall have gasket-type joints of spigot and socket or rebated form, unless otherwise described in the Contract.

3. Concrete jacking pipes shall comply with the relevant provisions of BS 5911: Part 120. Additionally, the Contractor shall ensure that the pipes can withstand the jacking loads to which they will be subjected during installation, without cracking or spalling. A certificate shall be supplied, confirming that the pipes are suitable for jacking and stating the distributed jacking loads for which they were designed.

(i) Particular requirements from the options listed in Appendix A of BS 5911: Parts 100, 110 or 120, should be described in the Contract.

(ii) Sub-clause 3 expressly provides for the Contractor to be responsible for the adequacy of the design of pipes for jacking insofar as it is relevant to his operations. See Clause 8(2) of the Sixth Edition.

(iii) IGN No. 4-12-01 deals with unreinforced and reinforced concrete pipes with flexible joints.

2.29 STEEL PIPES AND FITTINGS

1. Steel pipes, fittings and joints shall comply with the relevant provisions of BS 534 and BS 3601.

2. Pipes for cutting shall be clearly identified and used only as directed.

(i) The required grade and thickness of steel, together with the type and strength of pipe, should be described in the Contract.

(ii) Any requirement for coatings to steel pipes should be described in the Contract.

(iii) WIs No. 4-52-01 and IGN No. 4-52-02 deal with polymeric anti-corrosion (barrier) coatings.

2.30 PRESTRESSED CONCRETE PIPES AND FITTINGS

1. Prestressed concrete pressure pipes and fittings shall comply with the relevant provisions of BS 4625. Prestressed concrete pipes and fittings for drainage and sewerage purposes shall comply with the relevant provisions of BS 5178.

2. Unless steam cured, no pipes or fittings shall leave the place of manufacture until they have been allowed to cure and mature under suitable conditions for a total period of not less than 28 days. The surface finish shall be assessed in accordance and comply with the provisions of Clause 7.5 of BS 5911: Part 100.

(i) Particular requirements from the options listed in Appendix C of BS 4625 or Appendix A of BS 5178 should be described in the Contract.

(ii) The Contract should describe whether cylinder or non-cylinder type pipes and fittings are required.

2.31 DUCTILE IRON PIPES AND FITTINGS

(i) IGN No. 4-21-01 deals with ductile iron pipes and fittings.

1. Ductile iron pipes, fittings and joints shall comply with the relevant provisions of BS 4772.

(ii) IGN No. 4-51-01 deals with external zinc coating of ductile iron pipe, which BS 4772 now requires on all pipes in the diameter range 80 - 800 mm.

(iii) Wls No. 4-52-01 and IGN No. 4-52-02 deal with polymeric anti-corrosion (barrier) coatings.

2.32 UNPLASTICIZED PVC PIPES AND FITTINGS

(i) IGN No. 4-31-01 deals with unplasticized PVC pipes and fittings.

1. Unplasticized PVC pressure pipes joints and fittings shall comply with the relevant provisions as set out below:

(ii) The colour and size limitation for PVC-U pressure pipes are consistent with the current recommendations of the National Joint Utilities Group.

Material	Pipe	Joints and Fittings
PVC-U (Imperial grey)	BS 3505	BS 4346: Pt 1,3 (solvent welded) Pt2 (mechanical)
PVC-U (Metric blue)	Wls 4-31-06	Wls 4-31-07
MOPVC	Wls 4-31-08	BS 4346: Pt 1 Wls 4-31-07

(iii) Wls No. 4-31-06 calls for higher fracture toughness values than BS 3505.

Pipes for below ground use for potable water and having an outside diameter less than 75 mm shall be coloured blue.

2. Unplasticized PVC pipes, joints and fittings for gravity sewers and drains shall comply with the relevant provisions of BS 4660 or BS 5481.

3. Solid wall concentric external rib-reinforced unplasticized PVC sewer pipe shall comply with the relevant provisions of Wls No. 4-31-05.

4. Solvent cements for jointing unplasticized PVC pipes shall comply with BS 4346: Part 3. For pipes and fittings complying with BS 4660, solvent cement may alternatively comply with BS 6209.

2.33 ASBESTOS-CEMENT PIPES AND FITTINGS

(i) IGN No. 4-12-03 deals with asbestos-cement pipes and fittings.

1. Asbestos-cement pipes, joints and fittings for sewers shall comply with the relevant provisions for BS 3656.

2. Asbestos-cement pressure pipes, joints and bends shall comply with the relevant provisions of BS 486.

2.34 GLASS REINFORCED PLASTICS (GRP) PIPES AND FITTINGS

(i) IGN No. 4-34-01 deals with GRP pipes and fittings.

1. Glass e reinforced plastics (grp) pipes and fittings shall comply with the relevant provisions of BS 5480.

2.35 ACRYLONITRILE-BUTADIENE-STYRENE (ABS) PIPES AND FITTINGS

1. Acrylonitrile-butadiene-styrene (abs) pressure pipes and fittings shall comply with the relevant provisions of BS 5391: Part 1 and BS 5392: Part 1 respectively.

2.36 POLYETHYLENE PIPES AND FITTINGS

(i) The water industry's policy is that polyethylene pipe used for underground water supply purposes should be coloured blue.

(ii) BS 6730 deals with black polyethylene pipe for unprotected above ground use.

1. Blue polyethylene pipe up to nominal size 63 for below ground use for potable water shall comply with the relevant provisions of BS 6572.

2. Polyethylene pressure pipes for use for cold potable water or sewage in nominal sizes greater than 63 shall comply with the relevant provisions as set out below, except that for sewage rising mains below ground the colour shall be black.

Material	Colour	WIs No.
MDPE (below ground)	Blue	4-32-03
MDPE (above ground)	Black	4-32-09
HPPE (below ground)	Blue	4-32-13

3. Polyethylene fusion joints and fittings for use with cold potable water shall comply with the relevant provisions of WIs No. 4-32-04, or WIs No. 4-32-06.

4. Mechanical joints and fittings for polyethylene pipes for use with cold potable water shall comply with WIs No. 4-24-01.

2.37 PROPYLENE COPOLYMER PRESSURE PIPES

1. Propylene copolymer pressure pipe shall comply with the relevant provisions of BS 4991 and, where to be in contact with potable water, shall be Series 1.

2.38 RAINWATER PIPES AND GUTTERS

(i) The Contract should describe the section required for asbestos-cement, aluminium and PVC-U gutters.

(ii) The Contract should describe the required grade and shape of sheet and strip aluminium pipes and gutters.

(iii) BS 6087 deals with flexible joints for cast iron drainpipes and fittings.

(iv) The Contract should describe whether ears are required on cast iron pipes and fittings.

(v) The Contract should describe the required colour of PVC-U pipes and fittings.

1. Rainwater pipes, gutters, fixings and accessories shall comply with the relevant provisions of the appropriate British Standard, as set out below:

Material	BS
Cast iron	460, Type A
Asbestos-cement	569
Aluminium	2997
PVC-U	4576: Part 1

2.39 SOIL, WASTE AND VENTILATING PIPES

(i) BS 6087 deals with flexible joints for cast iron soil, waste and ventilating pipes and fittings.

1. Soil, waste and ventilating pipes, fittings and accessories for above-ground drainage systems shall comply with the relevant provisions of the appropriate British Standard, as set out below:

Material	BS
Cast iron	416, Parts 1 and 2
PVC-U (soil and ventilating)	4514
Polypropylene (waste)	5254
Plastics (waste)	5255

2. Wash basin and sink wastes shall comply with the relevant provisions of BS 3380.

3. Plastics waste traps shall comply with the relevant provisions of BS 3943.

(i) Water Supply Byelaws are relevant to water fittings used in connection with the supply and use of water.

(ii) The required class of plastics service pipes, pump delivery pipes and distributing pipes and fittings should be described in the Contract. Where copper is to be used, the required designation and condition should be described.

(iii) IGN No. 5-01-01 deals with the United Kingdom Water Fittings Byelaws Scheme.

(iv) Clause 2.49 deals with valves in larger sizes.

2.40   SERVICE SIZE WATER FITTINGS AND APPLIANCES

1. Service size water fittings and appliances shall comply with the relevant provisions of the appropriate specification, as set out in the following table:

Water fitting/appliance	Type/Material	BS/WIs No.
Service pipes, pump delivery pipes, distributing pipes and fittings	Copper Capillary and compression fittings for copper tubes	2871: Part 1 864: Part 2
	Polyethylene Copper and copper alloy compression fittings for polyethylene pipes Joints and fittings for polyethylene pipes (performance)	6572 WIs No. 4-22-01 and 4-32-11 864: Part 5 5114 3505
	PVC-U PVC-U joints and fittings (solvent welded) PVC-U joints and fittings (mechanical)	4346: Part 1 4346: Part 2
Draining taps	Screw-down pattern	2879
Draw-off taps	Metal bodied (performance) Plastics bodied (performance)	5412: Parts 1 - 5 5413: Parts 1 - 5
Stopvalves	Above-ground, screw-down pattern Underground	1010: Part 2 5433 WIs No. 4-23-04
Float operated valves	Diaphragm type (copper alloy body) Diaphragm type (plastics body)	1212: Part 2 1212: Part 3
Floats for ballvalves	Copper Plastics	1968 2456
Storage cisterns and lids	Low carbon steel Polyolefin or olefin copolymer	417: Part 2 4213
Wash basins	Ceramic Metal hand rinse	1188 1329
Sinks	Glazed fireclay Stainless steel	1206 1244: Part 2
WC pans	Horizontal outlet	5503: Parts 1 & 2
Connectors for WC pans	Plastics	5627
WC seats and covers	Plastics, Type 1	1254
WC flushing cisterns	Dual flush type	1125
Urinals	Stainless steel slab Vitreous china bowl	4880: Part 1 5520
Automatic flushing cisterns for urinals	Lidded	1876
Ferrules	Various	WIs No. 4-22-02

QUALITY ASSURED PRODUCTS PREFERRED — SEE CLAUSE 2.1

2.41 PTFE TAPE

1. Unsintered polytetrafluoroethylene (PTFE) tape for thread sealing applications shall comply with BS 4375.

2.42 MARKER TAPE

(i) Consideration should be given to the use of a marker tape and any requirements described in the Contract.

1. Marker tape for buried water mains shall be blue PVC or polyethylene mesh or ribbon at least 50 mm wide, incorporating a corrosion resistant tracing system.

2. Marker tape for buried cables shall be yellow PVC or polyethylene mesh or ribbon at least 150 mm wide. Ribbon shall be printed with the words 'ELECTRIC CABLE' in bold capital letters at intervals not exceeding 700 mm.

2.43 PIPES FOR LAND DRAINAGE AND TEMPORARY DRAINS

1. Pipes, joints and fittings for land drainage and temporary drains shall comply with the relevant provisions of the appropriate British Standard, as set out below:

Type	BS
'Perforated' or 'Surface water' vitrified clay pipes and fittings	65
Concrete porous pipes	5911: Part 114
Clayware field drain pipes	1196
Plastics pipes for use as light duty sub-soil drains	4962
Concrete pipes and fittings with ogee joints	5911: Part 110

2.44 PIPES FOR DUCTS

(i) BS 8313 gives guidance on ducts for building services.

(ii) Certain Public Utilities may require ducts to be of a particular colour. See also BS 1710.

1. Pipes, joints and fittings for exposed ducts for building services shall comply with the relevant provisions of the appropriate British Standard, as set out below:

Type	BS
Unplasticized PVC pipe	3505 or 3506
Hollow steel sections (greater than 150mm OD)	4360, 43C to 4848: Part 2
Steel tubes (not greater than 150mm OD)	6323: Part 2, HFW 2

2. Pipes, joints and fittings for buried ducts shall have flexible mechanical joints and comply with the relevant provisions of the appropriate British Standard, as set out below:

Type	BS
Vitrified clay	65
Asbestos-cement	3656
Unreinforced or reinforced concrete	5911: Part 100
Unplasticized PVC	4660 or 5481

2.45 DRAW CORD

1. Draw cord for duct threading shall be 8 mm diameter 3-strand hawser laid polypropylene rope complying with BS 4928.

2.46 JOINT SEALS AND LUBRICANTS

1. Elastomeric joint seals for water mains and drainage purposes shall be Types W and D respectively, complying with the relevant provisions of BS 2494, and shall be obtained from the pipe manufacturer.

2. Joint lubricants for sliding joints shall have no deleterious effects on either the joint rings or pipes, and be unaffected by the liquid to be conveyed. Lubricants to be used for jointing water mains shall not impart to water taste, colour, or any effect known to be injurious to health, and shall be resistant to bacterial growth.

(i) IGN No. 4-40-01 deals with the selection, properties, storage and installation requirements for elastomeric seals and sealing rings.

(ii) IGN No. EU14-001 (4-40-02) provides guidance for the selection, properties and use of elastomeric seals and sealing components.

2.47 FLANGES FOR PIPES AND PIPELINE FITTINGS

1. Flanges for pipes and pipeline fittings shall, unless otherwise required by the Contract, comply with BS 4504 Section 3.1 and 3.2 for 16 bar nominal pressure rating.

(i) Flanges in accordance with BS 4772 are dimensionally compatible with BS 4504: Sections 3.1 and 3.2

2.48 GASKETS FOR FLANGED JOINTS

1. Gaskets for flanged pipe joints shall be of the inside-bolt-circle type. The dimensions of gaskets shall comply with BS 4865: Part 1. Gaskets shall be manufactured from material complying with the provisions of BS 2494 for Type W rings.

(i) Any requirement for full face gaskets should be described in the Contract.

2.49 VALVES

1. Valves for pipeline installation shall comply with the relevant provisions of the appropriate British Standard, as set out below:

(i) Particular requirements from the options listed in the various Standards should be described in the Contract.

(ii) BS 6683 deals with the installation and use of valves.

(iii) IGN No. 4-23-01 deals with the selection, installation, operation and maintenance of isolating and boundary valves used in water distribution systems.

(iv) Clause 2.40 gives details of stopvalves.

Type	BS
Cast iron gate valves	5150
Cast iron gate (parallel slide) valves	5151
Cast iron check valves	5153
Copper alloy globe, globe stop and check, check and gate valves	5154
Butterfly valves	5155
Diaphragm valves	5156
Cast iron plug valves	5158
Predominantly key-operated cast iron gate valves for waterworks purpose	5163

2. Valve parts to be in contact with potable water shall meet the relevant provisions as set out below:

Type	BS/WIs No.
Metallic	DD 201
Non-metallic	BS 6920 IGN No. 5-01-02

2.50 PIPE SURROUND MATERIALS

1. Processed granular and as-dug bedding, sidefill and surround materials for buried pipelines shall comply with WIs No. 4-08-02.

(i) Any limitations on the size and type of materials should be described in the Contract.

(ii) IGN No. 4-02-01 gives guidance on pipe surround materials.

2.51 PRECAST CONCRETE SETTING BLOCKS FOR PIPES

1. Precast setting blocks for pipes shall have rectangular faces, with sufficient plan area to prevent punching of the blinding concrete or Final Surface and to provide an adequate seating for the pipes. They shall be manufactured from Grade C20 concrete using the same type of cement as in the adjacent concrete bed, and be cast in an approved mould. Blocks shall not be used until they have achieved a cube strength of 13.5 N/mm^2.

2.52 COMPRESSIBLE FILLER AND PACKING FOR PIPELINES

(i) BS 1142: does not give a range of insulating board thicknesses, but these are available commercially as 12 mm, 18 mm and 24 mm. For convenience, multiples of the 18 mm board have been specified.

1. Compressible filler for interrupting concrete protection to pipelines shall consist of bitumen impregnated insulating board to BS 1142 or other equally compressible material. The thickness of compressible filler shall be as follows:

Nominal bore of pipe (mm)	Thickness of compressible filler (mm)
Less than 450	18
450 - 1200	36
Exceeding 1200	54

2. Compressible packing for use between pipes and precast concrete setting blocks shall consist of bitumen damp-proof sheeting complying with BS 743.

2.53 CLAY PUDDLE

1. Clay puddle shall be impervious to water and be free from sand, grit, stones and other deleterious matter.

2. The clay on being dug shall be exposed to the air for at least 24 hours and thereafter shall be worked with water into a consistency suitable for punning. A roll of clay 300 mm long and 40 mm in diameter shall support its own weight when suspended from one end.

2.54 SEWER LININGS

(i) Appendix A of each WIs lists information to be established for particular design situations.

1. Sewer linings shall comply with the relevant provisions of the appropriate Water Industry specification (WIs) as set out below:

Type	WIs No.
Glassfibre reinforced cement (GRC)	4-12-04
Precast gunite	4-12-05
Precast and insitu ferrocement	4-12-06
Polyethylene (PE) pipes (non-pressure applications)	4-32-05
Non-circular polyethylene	4-32-10
Glassfibre reinforced plastics (GRP)	4-34-02
Polyester Insituform	4-34-04
Polyester resin concrete (PRC)	4-34-05

2.55 PRECAST CONCRETE MANHOLES AND SOAKAWAYS

(i) Particular requirements from the options listed in Appendix A of BS 5911: Part 200 should be described in the Contract.

1. Precast concrete manhole and soakaway units of circular cross section shall comply with the relevant provisions of BS 5911: Part 200. Units which bed onto bases shall be manufactured so that imposed vertical loads are transmitted directly via the full wall thickness of the unit. For joints between units and the underside of slabs, joint profiles shall be capable of withstanding applied loadings from such slabs and spigot-ended sections shall only be used where the soffit of the slab is recessed to receive them.

2.56 PRECAST CONCRETE COVER FRAME SEATING RINGS

1. Precast concrete cover frame seating rings shall comply with the relevant provisions of BS 5911: Part 200.

2.57 MANHOLE COVERS AND FRAMES

(i) If a particular shape of opening is required, this should be described in the Contract.

1. Manhole covers and frames shall comply with the relevant provisions of BS 497: Part 1 and have a minimum clear opening of 600 mm. Covers and frames with minimum clear openings outside the ranges in BS 497: Part 1 shall comply with the provisions of that Standard where applicable. All manhole covers shall have closed keyways.

2.58 MANHOLE STEP IRONS

(i) For all manholes except the precast concrete type, it will be necessary to describe the size and type of manhole step irons in the Contract.

1. Step irons for manholes and other chambers shall comply with the relevant provisions of BS 1247: Parts 1, 2 and 3 or WIs No. 4-33-01.

2.59 GULLIES AND GULLY COVER SLABS

(i) The Standard which is to apply for vitrified clay gullies should be described in the Contract.

1. Precast concrete gullies and gully cover slabs shall comply with the relevant provisions of BS 5911: Part 2.

2. Vitrified clay gullies shall comply with the relevant provisions of BS EN 295: Part 1 or BS 65.

2.60 GULLY COVERS, GRATINGS AND FRAMES

(i) Some Highway Authorities demand a particular slot configuration for gully gratings, depending upon the road gradient.

1. Gully covers, gratings and frames shall comply with the relevant provisions of BS 497: Part 1.

2.61 HYDRANTS

(i) Fire hydrants should be compatible with the requirements of the local Fire Service.

(ii) The required type of hydrant, dimensions of surface box frames and covers, and size, type and material of hydrant indicator plates should be described in the Contract.

(iii) Screw-down type hydrants with loose valve plungers may not permit the passage of swabs.

1. Hydrants, surface box frames and covers shall comply with the relevant provisions of BS 750.

2. Hydrant box covers shall be provided with recesses for lifting keys.

3. Hydrant indicator plates shall comply with the relevant provisions of BS 3251.

2.62 SURFACE BOXES AND GUARDS

(i) Particular requirements from the options listed in Appendix A of BS 5834: Part 1 should be described in the Contract, as should those from Appendix B of Parts 2 and 3.

1. Small and large surface boxes shall comply with the relevant provisions of BS 5834: Parts 2 and 3 respectively or WIs No. 4-37-01.

2. Guards and foundation units for underground stopvalves shall comply with the relevant provisions of BS 5834: Part 1 or WIs No. 4-37-01.

QUALITY ASSURED PRODUCTS PREFERRED — SEE CLAUSE 2.1

(i) The required type of cement should be described in the Contract.

(ii) Sub-clause 7 expressly provides for the Contractor to be responsible for the adequacy of the design of the segments, insofar as it is relevant to his operations. See Clause 8(2) of the Sixth Edition. A review of current test procedures for precast concrete tunnel linings can be found in CIRIA Technical Note 104.

2.63 PRECAST CONCRETE SEGMENTS FOR TUNNELS AND SHAFTS

1. The minimum 28 day characteristic strength of concrete used in the manufacture of segments shall be 40 N/mm^2.

2. Concrete shall be sampled and tested for compliance with the specified characteristic strength in accordance with the provisions of Part 4 of BS 5328. Sampling shall be at a rate of not less than one sample per 20 cubic metres of fresh concrete. All segments shall have the date of manufacture clearly marked in an appropriate position at the time of manufacture.

3. Segments shall not be removed from the moulds until the concrete cube strength has reached 10 N/mm^2 and no segments shall leave the place of manufacture or be used in the Works until 28 days after casting. Copies of test cube results shall be sent to the Engineer and segments shall not be incorporated into the Permanent Works until the Engineer is satisfied that the relevant test results confirm that the concrete complies with the specified characteristic strength.

4. Segments shall be cast with such accuracy and uniformity of dimensions that all similar segments shall be interchangeable, not only within individual rings, but with corresponding segments of other rings. All surfaces of the segments shall be free from cracking, honeycombing, or other blemishes.

5. Segments shall be manufactured to the following tolerances:

Nominal dimension	Permissible deviation (mm)
Circumferential length	±1.5
Radius of curvature	±3
Thickness	±3 (on back face only)
Width	±1.5

6. Segments shall be subjected to test for water absorption in accordance with the provisions of Clause 20.2 of BS 5911: Part 100.

7. The Contractor shall ensure that segments can withstand handling, erection, and any shield thrust stresses, without cracking, spalling or distortion.

8. The clear cover of concrete over any steel reinforcement shall be not less than 12 mm and spacers shall be of rustproof material.

9. All segment joint faces shall have a caulking rebate, which shall be of minimum size 20 mm deep by 3 mm wide for bolted segments and 10 mm deep by 3 mm wide for smooth-bore segments.

10. Where grouting is described in the Contract, all segments shall have at least one grout hole of 50 mm diameter.

11. Tapered segments for curves shall comply with the general requirements of this Clause, each segment having the radius and the location of the segment within the ring, clearly marked. Segments shall be symmetrically tapered.

2.64 BITUMINOUS JOINTING STRIP

1. Jointing strip for precast concrete tunnel and shaft segments shall be bitumen-based, 3 mm minimum thickness and be suitable for the size and type of segments with which it is to be used. Where bolt holes are required, they shall accurately match, in size and position, the corresponding holes in the segments.

2.65 PACKINGS FOR TUNNELS

1. Packing pieces for joint gaps in bolted tunnel segments shall be band-sawn, knot-free softwood, preserved in accordance with Clause 2.84.

2.66 GRUMMETS

1. Grummets shall be of gel-impregnated hemp or plastic and have a thickness before compression of not less than 10 mm. Grummets shall be a tight fit on, and shall have an external diameter at least 25 mm greater than, the bolts on to which they are fitted.

2.67 LEAD

1. The chemical composition of all lead to be used for jointing or caulking shall comply with the provisions of BS 1178.

2. Lead wool shall be extruded to produce strands of triangular cross section.

2.68 STRUCTURAL STEEL

1. Structural steel sections shall comply with the relevant provisions of the appropriate British Standard, as set out below:

Type	BS
Structural steel sections	4: Part 1
Cold rolled steel sections	2994
Weldable structural steels	4360
Hot-rolled structural steel sections	4848: Parts 2 and 4
Steel tubes for general purposes	6323: Parts 2 - 7

2.69 STEEL SHEET PILES

(i) The required grade of steel should be described in the Contract.

ii) The requirement for piles to be coated should be deleted if no part is to be exposed on completion of the Works.

1. Steel from which steel sheet piles are rolled shall comply with the relevant provisions of BS 4360.

2. Maximum rolling margins shall be 4% above and 2.5% below the calculated masses and 75 mm over and 50 mm under the required lengths.

3. Before being driven, permanent steel sheet piles shall be wire-brushed to remove loose rust and dirt and be coated with black tar-based paint complying with BS 1070, Type B, except that piles in contact with water to be used for potable supply shall be coated with black bitumen solution to BS 3416.

2.70 WROUGHT ALUMINIUM AND ALUMINIUM ALLOY

1. Wrought aluminium and aluminium alloys shall comply with the relevant provisions of the appropriate British Standard, as set out below:

Type	BS
Sections for structural purposes	1161
Plate, sheet and strip	1470
Drawn tube	1471
Bars, extruded round tubes and sections	1474
Ingots and castings	1490

2.71 ELECTRODES, FILLER RODS AND WIRES FOR WELDING

1. Electrodes, filler rods and wires for welding shall be compatible with the grade of steel to be welded.

2. Electrodes for the manual metal-arc welding of carbon and carbon manganese steel and stainless steel shall comply with the relevant provisions of BS 639 and BS 2926 respectively.

3. Electrode wires and fluxes for the submerged arc welding of carbon steel and medium tensile steel shall comply with the relevant provisions of BS 4165.

(i) BS 7475 does not apply to the welding of stainless steel tubes or to sections greater than 6 mm thick.

4. Filler rods and wires for the gas-shielded arc welding of ferritic steel, austenitic stainless steel and aluminium and aluminium alloy shall comply with the relevant provisions of BS 2901: Parts 1, 2 and 4 respectively.

5. Manual welding of stainless steel shall be by the inert-gas tungsten-arc process.

2.72 NUTS, SCREWS, WASHERS AND BOLTS

(i) Any protective coatings required should be described in the Contract.

1. Mild and high strength nuts, screws, washers and bolts shall comply with the relevant provisions of the appropriate British Standard, as set out below:

Type	BS
Black hexagon bolts, screws and nuts	4190
Metal washers for general purposes	4320
High strength friction grip bolts, nuts and washers	4395: Parts 1 - 3

2. Bolting for pipes and fittings shall comply with the relevant provisions of BS 4504: Sections 3.1 and 3.2, except that spheriodal graphite iron bolts for use with ductile iron pipes and fittings shall be manufactured from metal complying with the provisions of BS 2789 for Grade 500/7.

3. Bolt lengths shall be sufficient to ensure that nuts are full-threaded when tightened in their final position.

4. Stainless steel nuts, screws, washers and bolts shall be manufactured from Grade 316S31 steel complying with BS 970: Part 1 or BS 1449: Part 2.

5. Where bolting is incompatible with the material being fixed, suitable isolating washers and sleeves shall be used.

2.73 SAFETY CHAINS

1. Mild steel safety chain shall be 8 mm nominal size Grade M(4) non-calibrated chain, Type 1, complying with BS 4942: Part 2. After manufacture, mild steel safety chains shall be hot dip galvanized in accordance with BS 729.

2. Stainless steel safety chain shall be manufactured from Grade 316S31 steel complying with BS 970: Part 1. Chain links shall be welded and have an internal length not exceeding 45 mm and an internal width of between 12 mm and 18 mm. The fins caused by welding shall be removed and the weld shall be smoothly finished all round. When tested in accordance with Clause 7.3 of BS 4942: Part 2, each chain shall withstand a breaking force of 30 kN and a proof force of 15 kN.

(i) The loading requirement of Building - use Category 6 is consistent with Table 4 of BS 6399: Part 1 for industrial balustrades. The barrier height is 1100 mm.

(ii) Where stainless steel tubes are to be bent to very small radii, it may be necessary to describe their condition as GKM(S) instead of KM.

(iii) BS 6180 also deals with permanent protective barriers designed to resist vehicular impacts.

2.74 HANDRAILS AND BALUSTERS

1. Handrails and balusters shall be manufactured from material complying with the relevant provisions of the appropriate British Standard, as set out below. Protective barriers shall comply with the provisions of BS 6180 for Building - use Category 6.

Material	Handrails				Balusters			
	Solid		Tubular		Solid		Tubular	
	BS	Grade	BS	Grade	BS	Grade	BS	Grade
Mild steel	4360	43A	1387	-	4360	43A	1387	-
			or				or	
	-	-	6323 Pt2	HFW2	-	-	6323 Pt2	HFW2
Stainless steel	970 Pt1	316S31	6323 Pt8	LW17KM	970 Pt1	316S31	6323 Pt8	LW17KM
Aluminium	1474	6082	1474	6082	1490	LM6	1474	6082
			or				or	
	-	-	1471	6082	-	-	1471	6082

2. After manufacture, mild steel and aluminium handrails and balusters, shall be hot dip galvanized or anodised, as appropriate, in accordance with BS 729 or BS 1615, Grade AA25.

2.75 LADDERS

1. Low carbon steel ladders for vertical fixing shall comply with the relevant provision of BS 4211, Class A.

2. After fabrication, low carbon steel ladders shall be hot dip galvanized in accordance with BS 729.

3. Stainless steel ladders for vertical fixing shall be fabricated from Grade 316S31 steel complying with BS 970: Part 1 or BS 1449: Part 2 and shall comply with any dimensional provisions of BS 4211, Class A.

4. Aluminium ladders for vertical fixing shall be fabricated from Grade 6082 aluminium complying with BS 1474 and shall comply with any relevant provisions of BS 4211, Class A.

5. After fabrication, aluminium ladders shall be anodised in accordance with BS 1615, Grade AA25.

(i) The information required by Appendix B in each Part of BS 4592 should be described in the Contract.

(ii) BS 5395 gives guidance on the design and construction of stairs, ladders and walkways.

2.76 INDUSTRIAL FLOORING, WALKWAYS AND STAIR TREADS

1. Steel and aluminium industrial open type metal flooring, walkways and stair treads shall comply with the relevant provisions of BS 4592: Parts 1, 2 and 3.

2. After fabrication, low carbon steel flooring, walkways and stair treads shall be hot dip galvanized in accordance with BS 729.

(i) Sizes and types of fixings should be described in the Contract, together with minimum requirements for edge distances, centres of fixings and embedments.

(ii) For guidance on the selection and use of fixings in concrete and masonry, see CIRIA Technical Note TN 137 (1991).

(iii) BS 6180 gives recommendations for fixing protective barriers (see Clause 2.74).

(iv) BS 5080: Part 1 does not give recommendations on the interpretation of the results of tests for the purposes of design, selection or use of fixings. CIRIA Technical Note TN75 deals with loading tests on fixings in concrete.

2.77   FIXINGS FOR METALWORK

1. Mild steel bolts and nuts shall be hot dip galvanized in accordance with BS 729 and stainless steel bolts and nuts shall be manufactured from Grade 316S31 steel complying with BS 970: Part 1 or BS 1449: Part 2.

2. Stainless steel proprietary fixings shall be manufactured from Grade 316S31 steel complying with BS 970: Part 1 or BS 1449: Part 2. Mild and high tensile steel proprietary fixings shall be protected in accordance with the relevant provisions of the appropriate British Standard, as set out below:

Type of protection	Type of fixing		
	Cast-in, having no machined thread	Cast-in/expanding, basic major diameter of machined thread	
		Not exceeding 19mm	Exceeding 19mm
Hot dip galvanized	BS 729	-	-
Electroplated cadmium	BS1706, Cd 4	BS 3382: Pt 1	BS1706, Cd 4
Electroplated zinc	BS1706, Zn 10	BS 3382: Pt 2	BS1706, Zn 10

3. Where described in the Contract, axial and shear loading tests on structural fixings in concrete or masonry shall be carried out in accordance with the provisions of BS 5080: Parts 1 and 2 respectively. The safe working load shall be as described in the Contract.

4. Where fixings are incompatible with the material being fixed, suitable isolating washers and sleeves shall be used.

2.78   FIXING ACCESSORIES FOR BUILDING PURPOSES

1. Fixings for sheet, roof and wall coverings shall comply with the relevant provisions of BS 1494: Part 1.

2.79   NAILS

1. Nails shall comply with the relevant provisions of the appropriate British Standard, as set out below:

Type	BS
Steel	1202: Part 1
Copper	1202: Part 2
Aluminium	1202: Part 3

2.80   CONNECTORS FOR TIMBER

1. Connectors for timber shall comply with the relevant provisions of BS 1579.

2.81   JOIST HANGERS

1. Materials for joist hangers for building into masonry walls, or the inner skin of cavity walls, shall comply with the provisions of BS 6178: Part 1, Clause 3.1 (b).

5. Priming paint for wood shall comply with the relevant provisions of the appropriate British Standard, as set out below:

Type	BS
Ready mixed aluminium	4756, Type II
Water-borne	5082, Type B
Solvent-borne	5358, Type B

6. Priming paint for metal shall comply with the relevant provisions of the appropriate British Standard, as set out below:

Type	BS
Lead-based	2523, Type B or C
Calcium plumbate	3698, Type A
Metallic zinc-rich (organic media)	4652

7. Paint remover shall be non-flammable, solvent-based and comply with BS 3761.

2.95 PLASTER

1. Premixed lightweight plaster shall comply with the relevant provisions of BS 1191: Part 2. Final coats shall be Type b.1 and undercoats as set out below:

Application	Type
Brickwork and blockwork	a.1 or a.3
Concrete	a.3
Metal lathing	a.2

2. Polyvinyl acetate emulsion bonding agents for indoor use with BS 1191: Part 2, Type a.3 plaster shall comply with BS 5270: Part 1.

2.96 METAL LATHING

1. Expanded metal and ribbed lathing for internal plastering and external rendering respectively shall comply with the relevant provisions of BS 1369: Part 1.

2.97 EXPANDED METAL ANGLE BEADS

1. Expanded metal angle beads shall comply with the relevant provisions of BS 6452: Part 1.

2.98 BOARDS FOR PANELLING

(i) The required type, grade and thickness of board should be described in the Contract.

1. Boards for panelling shall comply with the relevant provisions of the appropriate British Standard, as set out in the following table:

QUALITY ASSURED PRODUCTS PREFERRED — SEE CLAUSE 2.1

Type	BS
Fibre building board - Medium board and hardboard	1142:
Fibre building board - Insulation board (softboard)	1142:
Gypsum plasterboard	1230: Part 1
Expanded polystyrene boards	3837: Part 1
Gypsum wallboard panels	4022
Rigid urethane foam - laminated board for building purposes	4841: Part 1
Rigid urethane foam - laminated board for use as a wall and ceiling insulation	4841: Part 2
Decorated laminated plastics sheet veneered boards and panels	4965
Wood chipboard	7331
Particle board	5669: Part 4

2.99   WALL TILES

1. Ceramic tiles for internal walls shall comply with the relevant provisions of BS 6431: Parts 1 - 9.

(i) In addition to the relevant Part of BS 6431 the type, size, thickness and colour of tiles should be described in the Contract.

2.100 FLOOR TILES

1. Floor tiles shall comply with the relevant provisions of the appropriate British Standard, as set out below:

(i) Facial sizes, thickness, colour and, in the cases of floor quarries, category, should be described in the Contract.

Type	BS
Ceramic	6431: Parts 1 - 9
Thermoplastic	2592
Semi-flexible PVC	3260
Unbacked flexible PVC	3261: Part 1
Terrazzo	4131

2.101 MASTIC ASPHALT

1. Mastic asphalt for building and civil engineering shall comply with the relevant provisions of BS 6925, T25, as set out below:

(i) Grade IV mastic asphalt flooring is suitable for loading sheds and heavy duty factory floors. Lower grades may be appropriate in other circumstances.

(ii) Mastic asphalts with natural rock asphalt aggregates will not normally be necessary.

(iii) Where an acidic environment is expected the Mastic Asphalt Council should be consulted for advice on suitability of limestone aggregates.

Application	Type
Roofing	R988
Flooring	F1076, Grade IV
Tanking	T1097
Coloured flooring	F1451, Grade IV

2.102 ROOF COVERINGS

1. Roof coverings shall comply with the relevant provisions of the appropriate British Standard, as set out in the following table:

(i) The required type, grade, category, classification, size, group or colour of roof covering material should be described in the Contract.

Material/Type	BS
Clay tiles and fittings	402: Part 1
Concrete tiles and fittings	473 & 550
Slates	680: Part 2
Asbestos-cement and cellulose - asbestos-cement flat sheets	690: Part 2
Asbestos-cement slates	690: Part 4
Asbestos-cement lining sheets and panels	690: Part 5
Felt	747

2.103 MINERAL AGGREGATES FOR FLAT ROOFS

1. Mineral aggregates for the reflection of solar heat on flat built-up bitumen or mastic asphalt roofs shall be light coloured and consist of a hard limestone having a low moisture absorption characteristic, granite, gravel, calcined flint, calcite or felspar, of 10 mm nominal size.

(i) This Clause is an amalgam of the recommendations of Clauses 3.14.1(4) and (5), and 2.9(1) of CP 144: Parts 3 and 4 respectively.

(ii) Where an acidic environment is expected the Mastic Asphalt Council should be consulted for advice on suitability of limestone aggregates.

2.104 FLASHINGS

1. Flashings shall comprise milled lead strip complying with BS 1178, Code No. 5.

(i) Any requirement for a different material, or thickness of sheet, should be described in the Contract.

2.105 BRICKS AND BLOCKS

1. Clay bricks, precast concrete masonry units and calcium silicate bricks shall comply with the relevant provisions of BS 3921, BS 6073: Parts 1 and 2 and BS 187 respectively.

2. Bricks to be used for manholes and chambers shall be solid type.

3. The shapes and dimensions of special bricks shall comply with the relevant provisions of BS 4729.

4. Air bricks and gratings for wall ventilation shall comply with the relevant provisions of BS 493 and shall match any surrounding bricks.

(i) The type, class and grade of bricks and blocks should be described in the Contract.

(ii) IGN No. 4-10-01 deals with bricks.

(iii) Particular requirements for airbricks and gratings from the options listed in Appendix A of BS 493 should be described in the Contract.

2.106 METAL TIES

1. Metal ties for cavity wall construction shall comply with the relevant provisions of BS 1243.

(i) British Standard DD140: Part 2 gives recommendations for the design of wall ties.

2.107 PERMANENT FENCING

1. Permanent fencing shall comply with the relevant provisions of the appropriate Part of BS 1722, as set out in the following table:

(i) Where appropriate, the various Parts of BS 1722 provide for concrete for surrounding the bases of posts.

Part of BS 1722	Type of fencing
1	Chain link fences
2	Woven wire fences
3	Strained wire fences
4	Cleft chestnut pale fences
5	Close boarded fences
6	Wooden palisade fences
7	Wooden post and rail fences
8	Mild steel (low carbon steel) continuous bar fences
9	Mild steel (low carbon steel) fences with round or square verticals and flat posts and horizontals
10	Anti-intruder chain link fences
11	Woven wood and lap boarded panel fences
12	Steel palisade fences
13	Chain link fences for tennis court surrounds
14	Open mesh steel panel fences

2. All timber for permanent fencing shall be given preservative treatment in accordance with the provisions of the relevant Part of BS 1722.

2.108 FIELD GATES

(i) Fittings and dimensions for gates should be described in the Contract.

1. Field gates, posts and fittings shall comply with the relevant provisions of BS 3470.

2. All timber for field gates and posts shall be given preservative treatment in accordance with the provisions of BS 3470.

3. All fittings and steel field gates and posts shall be hot dip galvanized in accordance with BS 729.

2.109 STILES, BRIDLE GATES AND KISSING GATES

1. Stiles, bridle gates and kissing gates shall comply with the relevant provisions of BS 5709.

2. All timber for stiles, bridle gates, kissing gates and posts shall be given preservative treatment in accordance with the provisions of BS 5709.

3. All fittings and steel stiles, bridle gates, kissing gates and posts shall be hot dip galvanized in accordance with BS 729.

4. Concrete for surrounding the bases of posts shall be Grade C20.

2.110 NATURAL STONE

(i) BS 5390 gives guidance on the choice of stone.

1. Natural stone shall be of durable quality, uniform in texture, and free from iron bands, spots, sandholes, flaws, shakes and other imperfections which would adversely affect its strength or appearance. The dimensions of stones shall be adequate for proper coursing and bonding.

2.111 DRESSED NATURAL STONE KERBS, CHANNELS, QUADRANTS AND SETTS

(i) The required size and type of setts should be described in the Contract.

1. New dressed granite and whinstone kerbs, channels, quadrants and setts shall comply with the relevant provisions of BS 435.

2. Second-hand stone kerbs, channels, quadrants and setts shall not be excessively weathered, worn or chipped, and shall be free from all bedding and jointing materials. Faces which are to remain exposed on completion of the Works shall be free from stains.

2.112 CAST STONE

(i) The type, constituent material and colour of cast stone should be described in the Contract.

1. Cast stone shall comply with the relevant provisions of BS 1217.

2. Reconstructed stone masonry units shall comply with the relevant provisions of BS 6457.

2.113 COPING UNITS

(i) The required type of cement for cast coping units should be described in the Contract.

(ii) In areas of high air pollution, Type A slate coping units will be required.

1. Precast concrete, cast stone, clayware, natural stone and slate coping units shall comply with the relevant provisions of BS 5642: Part 2. Slate coping units shall be Type B unless otherwise described in the Contract.

2.114 PRECAST CONCRETE KERBS, CHANNELS, EDGINGS AND QUADRANTS

1. Precast concrete kerbs, channels and edgings shall be hydraulically pressed and they, and precast concrete quadrants, shall comply with BS 7263: Part 1 Where kerbs or channels are required to be laid to a radius of 12 m or less, components of the appropriate radius shall be used.

2.115 PRECAST CONCRETE FLAGS AND PAVING BLOCKS

1. Precast concrete flags shall be hydraulically pressed and shall comply with the relevant provisions of BS 7263: Part 1. Unless otherwise described in the Contract, flags shall be 50 mm thick.

2. Precast concrete paving blocks shall comply with the relevant provisions of BS 6717: Part 1.

2.116 GENERAL FILLING MATERIALS

(i) Building Research Establishment Digest 276 deals with hardcore.

1. Hardcore shall consist of clean, hard, durable material, either broken stone, bricks or concrete, graded from 200 mm to 50 mm, and be free from extraneous matter.

2. Selected fill whether selected from locally excavated material or imported, shall consist of uniform readily compactible material, free from vegetable matter, building rubbish and frozen material, or materials susceptible to spontaneous combustion, and excluding clay of liquid limit greater than 80 and/or plastic limit greater than 55 and materials of excessively high moisture content. Clay lumps and stones retained on 75 mm and 37.5 mm sieves respectively shall be excluded from the fill material.

2.117 GRANULAR SUB-BASE MATERIAL

1. Granular sub-base material shall be natural sands, gravels, crushed rock, crushed slag, crushed concrete or well burnt non-plastic shale. The material shall be well graded and lie within the following grading limits:

QUALITY ASSURED PRODUCTS PREFERRED — SEE CLAUSE 2.1

BS 410 Test sieve	Percentage by mass passing	
	Type 1	Type 2
75mm	100	100
37.5mm	85 - 100	85 - 100
10mm	40 - 70	45 - 100
5mm	25 - 45	25 - 85
600µm	8 - 22	8 - 45
75µm	0 - 10	0 - 10

2. Where granular sub-base material is to be used within 450 mm of the surface of any road, the Contractor shall supply to the Engineer a certificate confirming that the material has a heave not greater than 15 mm when subjected to the frost test as specified in BS 812: Part 124 as amended by Clause 705 of the Department of Transport's 'Specification for Highway Works'.

3. Natural sands and gravels shall only be permitted in Type 2 material.

4. The particle size shall be determined by the washing and sieving method of BS 812: Part 103. The material passing a 425 µm BS sieve, when tested in accordance with BS 1377: Part 2, shall be non-plastic for Type 1 and have a Plasticity Index of less than 6 for Type 2.

5. With the exception of well burnt non-plastic shale, the material shall have a 'ten per cent fines' value of 50 kN or more when tested in accordance with BS 812: Part 111.

2.118 WET-MIX MACADAM

1. Wet-mix macadam shall consist of crushed rock or crushed slag, graded in accordance with the following table:

BS 410 test sieve	Percentage by mass passing
50mm	100
37.5mm	95 - 100
20mm	60 - 80
10mm	40 - 60
5mm	25 - 40
2.36mm	15 - 30
600µm	8 - 22
75µm	0 - 8

2. The particle size shall be determined by the washing and sieving method of BS 812: Part 103.

3. Aggregate quality and cleanliness shall comply with the relevant requirements of Clause 2.10. The flakiness index shall be less than 35 when determined in accordance with BS 812: Part 105, Section 105.1.

4. The moisture content of the wet-mix macadam shall be the optimum ±0.5% as determined in accordance with BS 5835: Part 1.

2.119 COATED MACADAM

1. Coated macadam for roads and other paved surfaces shall comply with the relevant provisions of BS 4987: Part 1.

2.120 ROLLED ASPHALT

1. Hot rolled asphalt shall comply with the relevant provisions of BS 594: Part 1.

2.121 BITUMEN ROAD EMULSIONS

1. Bitumen road emulsions shall comply with the relevant provisions of BS 434: Part 1.

2.122 DOWEL BARS

1. Dowel bars for expansion joints in concrete shall consist of mild steel complying with the provisions of BS 4449, Grade 250.

2. Dowel bars shall be straight, free from burrs or other irregularities and shall have their sliding ends sawn. The sliding half of each dowel bar shall be painted with a thin coat of bond breaking compound, and the end of this half shall be provided with a close fitting plastic or waterproof cardboard cap at least 100 mm long, the end 20 mm of which shall be fitted with a disc of joint filler or a pad of cotton waste.

2.123 BOND BREAKING COMPOUND FOR DOWEL BARS

1. Bond breaking compound for dowel bars shall consist of a bitumen paint containing 66% of 200 pen bitumen, blended hot with 14% light creosote oil with the addition, when cold, of 20% solvent naptha. It shall in no way retard or otherwise affect the setting of concrete.

2.124 JOINT FILLER BOARD

1. Filler board for joints in concrete (other than softwood) shall comply with the tests in Clause 1015.1 of the Department of Transport's 'Specification for Highway Works'. Knot-free softwood, preserved in accordance with Clause 2.84 may be used for joints in concrete carriageways.

2. Holes in preformed joint filler to accommodate dowel bars shall be accurately bored or punched out to produce a sliding fit on the dowel bars.

3. The material comprising the joint filler shall be of such quality that it can be satisfactorily installed in position at the joint.

4. Adhesives used to retain preformed joint fillers in place during construction shall have no harmful effects on concrete and, except for those used in connection with softwood fillers, shall be obtained from the same manufacturer as the joint filler.

5. Preformed filler for joints in structures to retain aqueous liquids shall have a maximum water absorption of 0.3% by volume and a non recovered compression set of 20% of the original thickness, both when tested in accordance with ASTM D3595.

2.125 JOINT SEALING COMPOUNDS AND SEALANTS

(i) Fuel-resistant types of sealants to BS 2499 or BS 5212: Part 1 may be required where concrete surfaces are subject to regular fuel spillage.

1. Joint sealing compounds shall comply with the requirements of Wls No. 4-60-01 and shall be impermeable ductile materials of a type suitable for the conditions of exposure in which they are to be placed, and capable of providing a durable, flexible and watertight seal by adhesion to the concrete throughout the range of joint movement.

2. Hot poured joint sealants shall comply with BS 2499, Ordinary Type A1 sealant.

3. Cold poured polymer-based joint sealants shall comply with BS 5212: Part 1, Normal Type N sealant.

QUALITY ASSURED PRODUCTS PREFERRED — SEE CLAUSE 2.1

(ii) There are no current British Standards for the cold-applied non-curing and heat-softened hand-applied types of sealant, though various such materials are available in proprietary form.

(iii) BS 6213 gives guidance on the selection of constructional sealants.

(iv) In certain circumstances polyurethane-based sealants (for which there are no current British Standards) may be more resistant to biodegradation than poly-sulphide-based ones.

(v) CIRIA Technical Notes TN128 and TN144 deal with civil engineering sealants in wet conditions.

4. Two-part polysulphide-based sealants shall comply with the relevant provisions of BS 4254. Pouring Grade shall be applied to horizontal upward-facing joints and Gun Grade to joints of any other aspect or inclination. Other two-part polymer-based sealants of Gun or Trowel Grade shall comply with the physical and test requirements of BS 4254.

5. Silicone based building sealants shall comply with the relevant provisions of BS 5889.

6. Primers for use with joint sealants shall be compatible with, and obtained from the same manufacturers as, the adjacent sealant. Primers shall have no harmful effects on concrete.

7. Sealants and primers which will be in contact with water to be used for potable supply shall not impart to water taste, colour, or any effect known to be harmful to health, and shall be resistant to bacterial growth.

8. Sealants and primers which will be in contact with sewage or sewage sludge shall be resistant to biodegradation.

2.126 WATERSTOPS

(i) The properties of PVC waterstops are temperature and formulation dependent. Manufacturers' recommendations for storage, handling, installation and use, particularly at temperatures below $0^{o}C$, should be obtained.

(ii) IGN No. 4-31-03 gives guidance on joint design and installation of PVC waterstops in water retaining structures.

1. Plasticized PVC waterstops shall comply with the relevant provisions of WIs No. 4-31-02.

2. Rubber waterstops shall have the following properties when tested in accordance with the relevant Part of BS 903:

Part of BS 903	Property	Requirements
A1	Density	$1100 kg/m^3$ (±5%)
A26	Hardness	60 - 70 IRHD
A2	Tensile strength	not less than $17.5 N/mm^2$
A2	Elongation at break point	not less than 450%
A16	Water absorption (48 hours immersion)	not exceeding 5%

3. Rubber waterstops shall be suitable for storage, handling, installation and service within a temperature range of $0^{o}C$ to $+40^{o}C$.

2.127 DAMP PROOF COURSE

(i) BS 743 provides for damp proof courses of materials other than bitumen, except for polythene, which is covered by BS 6515.

1. Damp proof course shall be bitumen with hessian base complying with BS 6398, Class A.

SECTION 3

EXCAVATION, BACKFILLING AND RESTORATION

General Note

In respect of excavation, backfilling and reinstatement in streets this section incorporates the requirements of the Street Works (Reinstatement) Regulations 1992 and the Statutory Code of Practice entitled 'Specification for the Reinstatement of Openings in Highways' June 1992 (the HAUC specification), published by HMSO, both made under Section 71 of the New Roads and Street Works Act 1991.

In addition to the provisions of Sections 70 - 73 of the New Roads and Street Works Act 1991 in respect of reinstatement the following provisions of the Act are also relevant:

Section 65 - Safety measures
Section 66 - Avoidance of unnecessary delay or obstruction
Section 67 - Qualifications of Supervisors and Operatives
Section 68 - Facilities to be afforded to Street Authorities.

3.1 EXCAVATION

General

(i) The following publications give recommendations as to standards of good practice for excavation:

(a) BS 6031

(b) BS 6164

(c) Report R97, 'Trenching Practice' published by CIRIA.

(d) Technical Note TN95 'Proprietary trench support systems', published by CIRIA

(ii) CESMM requires a definition of 'rock' to be given, where required, in the Preamble to the Bill of Quantities.

(iii) The term 'Final Surface' is defined in CESMM.

(iv) Any special requirements for Site clearance or for the disposal of excavated materials should be described in the Contract.

(v) The Contract should describe the extent of any excavations where battered sides will be permitted. A detail of the allowable cross-section should be given.

(vi) Excavation in carriageways should wherever possible be located such that the edge of the opening is at least 1 m from the edge of the carriageway.

1. The Contractor shall carry out his operations in such a manner as to avoid damage to, or deterioration of, the Final Surfaces of excavations.

2. Excavation in streets shall be carried out in accordance with the relevant provisions of the HAUC 'Specification for the Reinstatement of Openings in Highways'.

3. If the Contractor encounters ground in the Final Surface which he considers unsuitable, or if the Final Surface is damaged or allowed to deteriorate, the Engineer shall be promptly informed.

4. The sides of excavations shall be adequately supported at all times and, except where described in or permitted under the Contract, shall not be battered.

5. The Contractor shall be responsible for the disposal of surplus excavated material off Site but no excavated material suitable for re-use in the Works shall be removed from the Site except on the direction, or with the permission, of the Engineer.

Trenches

6. Trenches in rock for pipes up to 100 mm nominal bore shall be excavated to provide a minimum clearance of 100 mm around the outside of pipe barrels and joints. For pipes with nominal bores exceeding 100 mm, the minimum clearance shall be increased to 150 mm for flexible pipeline and to 200 mm for rigid pipeline.

7. Trenches for pipes carrying water under pressure shall, except where otherwise described in the Contract, be excavated to a sufficient depth to ensure a minimum cover of 900 mm to the top of the pipes.

Headings, tunnels and shafts

8. When excavating headings, tunnels and shafts, the Contractor shall provide sufficient spoil storage capacity to avoid the need to remove excavated material from shaft sinking, heading or tunnel driving compounds between 19.00 hours on any day and 07.00 hours on the following day.

(vii) CESMM provides for the measurement of probing ahead and temporary support in tunnels; items should be billed for these requirements.

(viii) Excavated material for disposal off Site would normally be classified as controlled waste and the Employer, under the Environmental Protection Act 1990, has a duty of care to ensure that the Contractor complies with the legislation relating to the treatment, keeping or disposal of such material.

9. It shall be the responsibility of the Contractor to decide the need for, and to undertake, any ground investigation ahead of the face of any tunnel, heading or shaft, additional to that described in the Contract.

10. Excavations for headings and tunnels shall be adequately supported at all times. The faces of all headings and tunnels, other than in solid rock, shall be fully boxed whenever excavation has been, or will be, stopped for a period exceeding 12 hours.

11. All working shafts shall, unless otherwise permitted, be supplied with speaking tubes or telephones in communication with the Works below ground. Such tubes or telephones shall be provided with coloured light signalling systems.

3.2 TURF FOR RELAYING

1. Turves to be relaid shall measure approximately 1 m by 300 mm when cut and shall be of uniform thickness not less than 40 mm.

2. Turves shall be green when cut; they shall be kept moist and shall be laid within one week of cutting during the period 1 April to 31 August, or within two weeks of cutting during the remainder of the year.

3. The level of topsoil beneath turves shall be such that the final grass surface after compaction shall be flush with the adjoining grass surface.

3.3 TOPSOIL FOR RE-USE

(i) It is advisable to make an assessment of soil stacking requirements in cases where topsoil quality is important, and to provide accordingly in the Contact.

1. 'Topsoil' shall mean the top layer of soil that can support vegetation. It shall include all turf not required for relaying or not acceptable for turfing under Clause 3.2.

2. Topsoil shall be removed from the areas prescribed in the Contract and, where required for re-use, shall be stock-piled separately and kept free from weeds.

3.4 DEALING WITH WATER

1. The Contractor shall not allow water to lie in any part of the Works unless required to do so under the Contract; water arising from or draining into the works shall be drained or pumped to an approved disposal point. Any drainage sumps required shall, where practicable, be sited outside the area excavated for the Permanent Works, and shall be re-filled with concrete Grade C7.5 to the level of the underside of the adjacent permanent Works.

2. The Contractor shall take all necessary precautions to prevent any adjacent ground from being adversely affected by loss of fines through any de-watering process.

3. The Contractor shall take all necessary precautions to prevent any ground water from entering mains to be used for the conveyance of potable water.

3.5 TEMPORARY DRAINS

1. Where temporary drains are required, they shall be laid in a narrow trench or grip formed below the bottom of the excavation in an approved position. The pipes shall be open-jointed and shall be surrounded with free-draining granular material.

2. Grouting pipes shall be inserted in the line of the temporary drains at intervals not exceeding 25 m and the drains shall be solidly filled with grout, Class G3 or G4, the grout pipes being cut off on completion.

3.6   USE OF COMPRESSED AIR

(i) See also Clause 1.17.1.

Standby plant

1. Where compressed air working is carried out, standby plant shall be installed of sufficient capacity to maintain the required air pressure if, at any time, all or part of the main plant is out of use. The standby plant shall include a power source independent of the main source.

2. The Contractor shall test all standby plant weekly by using it to supply air to the Works under normal working conditions.

Pressure control

3. The Contractor shall maintain such air pressures as may be necessary for safe working and shall provide facilities for varying the pressure accordingly.

Pressure gauges

4. In addition to the gauges required by the 'Medical Code of Practice for Work in Compressed Air (Third Edition) 1982 reprinted with amendments 1992', (CIRIA Report R44) further pressure gauges shall be installed in every working chamber showing the pressure in the chamber and in the adjacent manlock.

Telephones

5. Each manlock or decompression chamber shall be connected by telephone to the manlock attendant's post, which shall also be connected by telephone to the compressor house attendant's post.

6. Telephone linked to a public telephone exchange shall be provided at the compressor house and at the top of each shaft at which work is being carried out or from which a tunnel is being driven.

Provision of safety valves and testing of plant

7. The air locks, medical locks, bulkheads, pipes and other apparatus to be used for compressed air working shall be capable of withstanding twice the maximum pressure to be used.

8. After installation, but before work in compressed air is commenced, compressed air plant shall be given a 24-hour continuous running test at the normal operating pressure and shall operate satisfactorily for this period.

9. Each air receiver shall be fitted with a safety valve, which shall be set to blow at a pressure to be agreed with the Engineer.

3.7   BACKFILLING

1. Backfilling shall, wherever practicable, be undertaken immediately the specified operations preceding it have been completed. Backfilling shall not, however, be commenced until the works to be covered have achieved a strength sufficient to withstand all loading imposed thereon.

2. Backfilling around Permanent Works shall be undertaken in such manner as to avoid uneven loading or damage.

3. Filling material to excavations not situated in highways or prospective highways shall be in accordance with Clause 2.116.2, deposited in layers not exceeding 250 mm unconsolidated thickness and compacted to form a stable backfill.

(i) Any special requirements for backfilling around mains and services should be described in the Contract.

4. Excavations in streets shall be filled, above the level of any pipe surround required in accordance with the HAUC 'Specification for the Reinstatement of Openings in Highways'.

(ii) Any particular requirements for the materials to be used for backfilling should be described in the Contract.

5. Where the excavations have been supported and the supports are to be removed, these, where practicable, shall be withdrawn progressively as backfilling proceeds in such a manner as to minimise the danger of collapse, and all voids formed behind the supports shall be carefully filled and compacted.

3.8 REINSTATEMENT OF MAINTAINABLE HIGHWAYS

Reinstatement of carriageways, footways, footpaths, cycle tracks and verges.

(i) Any particular requirements for the reinstatement method, materials and depths of layers should be described in the Contract.

1. Reinstatement of streets which are maintainable highways shall be undertaken in accordance with the relevant provisions of the HAUC 'Specification for the Reinstatement of Openings in Highways'.

Reinstatement of kerbs, channels, edgings and quadrants

2. Kerbs, channels, edgings and quadrants disturbed by the Works shall be relaid with existing units, providing they are not damaged. Where existing units are not suitable for re-use, the Contractor shall provide replacement units of similar texture, colour and type, consistent with those adjacent and complying with the relevant provisions of Clause 2.111 or 2.114 as appropriate.

3. The re-laying of kerbs, channels, edgings and quadrants shall be in accordance with Clause 8.10. In-situ kerbs and channels shall be reinstated to conform with adjoining kerbs and channels.

Reinstatement of manholes and surface boxes

4. The frames of all manholes and surface boxes shall be reinstated by bedding and haunching in Class M1 mortar unless, in the case of surface boxes, they are to seat in the recess of an appropriate precast concrete section. Frame tops shall be flush with the adjoining surface on all sides.

3.9 REINSTATEMENT OF NON-MAINTAINABLE HIGHWAYS

(i) Where the HAUC Specification is inappropriate, the reinstatement should be described in the Contract.

1. Non-maintainable highways shall, except where otherwise described in the Contract, be reinstated in accordance with the relevant provisions of Clause 3.8.

3.10 REINSTATEMENT OF UNPAVED LAND

(i) Any special grass seed mixtures required, differing from those specified in Clause 2.6, should be described in the Contract.

1. On completion of work in unpaved land the Contractor shall break up the surface of all land affected, to a depth of at least 300 mm, before replacing top soil, and shall cultivate and restore the land as closely as possible to its original condition.

(ii) Any requirements to apply fertiliser should be described in the Contract.

2. Surfaces to be sown with grass seed shall be reduced to a fine tilth and cleared of stones and extraneous material greater than 50 mm in size. The seed shall be sown at the proper seasons, evenly distributed and applied at a rate of not less than the quantities given in the following table:

Nature of area to be seeded	Level surfaces (g/m^2)	Sloping surfaces to cuttings and embankments (g/m^2)
Lawns	60	-
Surrounds to tanks and process plants	25	35
Agricultural land and roadside verges	6	10

(iii) See also Note C4 under Class E of CESMM. Any requirements of grass cutting and weed killing should be described in the Contract.

3. Surfaces to be turfed shall be prepared as for seeding. The approved turves shall be placed, butted, interlocked and tamped and the joints filled with fine sandy soil. On sloping ground where they may be likely to slip, turves shall be laid diagonally. Any subsidence taking place shall be made good by taking up the turf, filling with good finely sieved top soil and replacing the turf in the manner specified above. Any turf that dies shall be replaced with new turf.

3.11 TREES

1. The planting, staking and maintenance of trees in the advanced nursery stock category shall be carried out in accordance with the relevant provisions of BS 4043.

2. The preparation, planting and securing of semi-mature trees shall be carried out in accordance with the relevant provisions of BS 4043 and their subsequent maintenance shall comply with Section 4 of BS 5837.

3. Tree surgery, repair work, bracing and feeding, and tree removal shall be carried out in accordance with the relevant provisions of BS 3998.

4. Measures to protect and preserve existing trees to be retained on the Site shall be taken in accordance with the relevant provisions of BS 5837.

3.12 LAND DRAINS

(i) Any special requirements necessary to facilitate the restoration of land drainage should be described in the Contract.

1. The positions of all land drains intercepted or disturbed shall be prominently marked at every point of intersection with the work. The Contractor shall record these positions, depths, pipe diameters and the types of construction, and a copy of these records shall be given to the Engineer. Care shall be taken during the progress of the Works to prevent the disturbance of markers.

2. Prior to the permanent reinstatement of land drainage the Contractor shall clear the ends of existing drains, where intercepted by excavations, and shall afford facilities to the Engineer and the landowner or occupier to inspect them and determine the extent of replacement that may be necessary.

3. The backfill of intercepting excavations shall be compacted in 200 mm layers, to give a firm bearing immediately before replacement pipes are laid and shall be brought up to the level of the underside of the land drains or of any support to be provided.

4. The affected land drains shall be cut back into firm ground until, in each case, a section is exposed which is unaffected by the Works.

5. Replacement pipes or support beams shall bear on undisturbed ground for at least 500 mm at each end. The replacement pipes shall be of the same internal diameter as the sections of drain which they replace and shall be properly connected at each end.

6. Records shall be kept of all drainage system reinstatement work carried out, and a copy shall be given to the Engineer.

(i) This is a general clause to cover filling which performs no specific load-bearing or structural role. A more thorough specification may be necessary in other cases (see for instance the Department of Transport's 'Specification for Highway Works).

(i) It may be necessary for the Contract to describe safe values for vibrational amplitude and peak particle velocity.

3.13   FILLING ABOVE GROUND

1. Embankments and other areas of fill shall be formed of suitable materials capable of normal compaction to form a stable fill, deposited and compacted as soon as practicable after excavation, in layers of thickness appropriate to the compaction plant used.

2. The filling shall, where practicable, be built up and compacted evenly, and shall be maintained at all times with a sufficient camber or cross fall and a surface sufficiently even to enable surface water to drain readily from it.

3.14   BLASTING

1. The written consent of the Engineer shall be obtained for each proposal of the Contractor to use explosives.

2. Where blasting is proposed adjacent to a building or other structure, existing or under construction, the Contractor shall satisfy the Engineer that safe values of vibrational amplitude and peak particle velocity will not be exceeded.

3. The Contractor shall comply with the provisions of BS 6657 in respect of the use of electrical detonators in the vicinity of of static and mobile radio transmitters, including normal radio and television broadcasting stations and radar units associated with aircraft movements.

4. The handling, transport and use of explosives shall be in accordance with the relevant provisions of BS 5607. Explosives shall be used in the quantities and manner recommended by the manufacturers.

ASSOCIATED TOPICS

1.   DEMOLITION:

For demolition, see BS 6187 and BS 8004.

2.   PILING:

For piling see the Specification for Piling and associated guidance on contract documentation and measurement, published by the Institution of Civil Engineers.

SECTION 4

CONCRETE AND FORMWORK

(i) The provisions of this Section take account of BS 8007 and BS 8110 where appropriate.

4.1 CONCRETE

1. Concrete shall, except where otherwise described in the Contract, be produced transported and assessed for compliance with the Specification in accordance with the relevant provisions of BS 5328: Parts 3 and 4.

4.2 READY-MIXED CONCRETE

1. Where concrete is to be obtained from a ready-mix supplier, the Contractor shall obtain the Engineer's approval of the source and shall satisfy the Engineer that the supplying plant is approved by a third party certification body accredited under Category 2 (Product Conformity) by the National Accreditation Council for Certification Bodies.

(i) Any restrictions on the use of ready-mixed concrete in the Works should be described in the Contract.

(ii) A coded description for the concrete, to obviate unnecessary repetition of items upon delivery tickets may be acceptable to the Engineer.

(iii) Any requirements for information concerning the taking of test cubes or slump or other workability factor determinations, should be described in the Contract.

(iv) The provisions of Clause 4.2.1 are consistent with the Quality Assurance recommendations of BS 8110, Clause 2.3.

(v) Any restrictions on the use of admixtures in the Works should be described in the Contract (see Clause 5.3 of BS 5328: Part 2).

2. The Contractor shall also inform the Engineer what alternative suppliers are available to him if the approval of the source referred to above has to be withdrawn by the Engineer during the currency of the Contract.

3. The delivery ticket required for each load of ready-mixed concrete shall, in addition to the information prescribed under BS 5328: Part 3, detail:

(a)   the type and nominal maximum size of aggregate

(b)   the type or name and proportion of any admixture,

(c)   the actual cementitious content and the percentage of any pfa or ggbs included, and

(d)   the position of the concrete in the Works.

4. All delivery tickets shall be kept at the Site and shall be made available for inspection by the Engineer.

4.3 CONCRETE MIXES

1. Prescribed, Standard and Designated mixes shall be in accordance with Section 3, 4 or 5 of BS 5328: Part 2 respectively. The information specified under Clause 3.1 of BS 5328: Part 3 shall be given to the Engineer in every case, not less than 7 days before the start of concrete production. Further information specified in Clauses 3.2 and 3.3 of BS 5328: Part 3 shall also be given to the Engineer at appropriate times.

(i) If the rates given in the table in Clause 4.3.6 are not appropriate then the frequency of sampling should be described in the Contract.

(ii) The characteristic compressive strength described in the Contract should be selected, where possible, to achieve the required minimum cementitious content. If the relevant information is not available, trial mixes should be required to establish the required characteristic strength; and if aggregates to be used are too weak to produce the characteristic strength needed for high grade concrete, an alternative basis of assessing the cementitious content will be required.

2. Before concrete of a Designed mix is supplied, the Contractor shall, not less than 7 days before the start of the concrete production, provide all pertinent information specified in Clauses 3.1 to 3.5 inclusive of BS 5328: Part 3.

(iii) Where it is important that concrete should attain its maximum impermeability within 6 months of placing, a maximum free water/ cementitious ratio less that 0.6 will be required, and should be described in the Contract.

3. Unless otherwise described in the Contract, the cementitious content of concrete shall not exceed 400 kg/m^3 or 450 kg/m^3 where pfa forms a cementitious component and the structure is designed to retain an aqueous liquid. In any structural member, the maximum water/cementitious ratio and the minimum cementitious content of the concrete mix shall be in accordance with the following table, for the relevant exposure condition and nominal cover. Concrete in members of structures that are to retain an aqueous liquid shall have a maximum free water/ cementitious ratio of 0.55.

(iv) The figures given in the table in Clause 4.3.3 are taken from those in Table 3.4 of BS 8110: Part 1; for a description of the exposure conditions see Table 3.2 of that Standard. The exposure condition should be described in the Contract. For the very severe exposure condition air entrainment should be considered.

Exposure condition	Nominal cover (mm)			
Mild	20	20	20	20
Moderate	35	30	25	20
Severe	-	40	30	25
Very severe	-	50	40	30
Max; free water/cementitious ratio	0.60	0.55	0.50	0.45
Min; cementitious content (kg/m^3)	300	325	350	400

(v) Where there is the likelihood of unacceptable damage from alkali-silica reaction, specific precautions to minimise it should be described in the Contract in accordance with the recommendations of Technical Report TR30 'Alkali-Silica Reaction - Minimising the Risk of Damage to Concrete', published by the Concrete Society in October 1987 and BRE Digest 330 published by the Building Research Establishment in March 1988. Guidance relating to alkali-silica reaction is contained in Clause 4.2.4 of BS 5328: Part 1.

4. Where the Contract requires aggregates of nominal size other than 20 mm to be used, the minimum cementitious content in Clause 4.3.3 shall be modified as follows:

Nominal maximum aggregate size (mm)	Adjustments to minimum cementitious content in Clause 4.3.3 (kg/m^3)
10	+40
14	+20
40	-30

5. The maximum size of aggregate in any structural member shall not exceed 25% of the minimum thickness of the member.

(vi) The figures in the table in Clause 4.3.4 are taken from those in Table 3.3 of BS 8110: Part 1.

6. The frequency of sampling shall, except where otherwise described in the Contract, be as follows:

Type of structure	Sample to represent a volume of (m^3)
Critical structures	10
Intermediate structures	50
Heavy concrete construction	100

(vii) Guidance on concrete mix design is contained in BRE Report BR 106 'Design of normal concrete mixes' revised and re-published by the DoE in 1988.

(viii) Examples of the type of structure in sub-clause 6 are:
Critical structures: cantilevers,
columns,
suspended slabs
Intermediate structures:
beams,
ground slabs,
bridge decks,
walls

Heavy concrete construction:
foundations,
solid rafts

4.4   TRIAL MIXES

1. Where trial mixes are required, three separate batches of concrete shall be made using materials typical of the proposed source of supply and, where practicable, under fullscale production conditions. The suitability of the proposed mix proportions of Designed mixes to meet the specified strength shall be determined in accordance with Clause 3.4.3 of BS 5328: Part 3.

(i) Where it is not practicable to carry out full scale trials, special reference should be made in the Contract to laboratory scale mixes.

2. The workability of each of the trial batches shall be determined and three cubes made from each batch for test at 28 days.

(ii) Sufficient information should be derived from the trial mixes to ensure that the concrete will meet the specified requirements, including optional items under Clause 5.3 of BS 5328: Part 2. It may also be necessary to specify water absorption tests for structures designed to retain an aqueous liquid.

3. Additional sets of cubes from each batch may be required for tests at an earlier age.

4. The suitability of the proposed mix proportions of Designed mixes to meet the specified maximum free water/cementitious ratio shall be determined in accordance with Clause 3.5 of BS 5328: Part 3.

4.5   CONCRETE MIXES CONTAINING PFA

(i) Clause 2.15.1 details the allowable proportions of pfa.

1. The free water/cementitious ratio of concrete mixes containing pfa shall be reduced in relation to the pfa content, consistent with maintenance of the required workability, and shall not exceed 0.50 for concrete designed to retain an aqueous liquid.

(ii) Where high replacement levels are used special care will be required in striking formwork and with curing.

2. Sulfate-resisting cement shall not be used in concrete mixes containing pfa.

4.6   CONCRETE MIXES CONTAINING GGBS

(i) Clause 2.15.1 details the allowable proportions of ggbs; the higher percentage for the special use to resist sulfate attack is consistent with the recommendations of Clause 6.2.1 of BS 8007.

1. Sulfate-resisting cement shall not be used in concrete mixes containing ggbs.

(ii) Where high replacement levels are used special care will be required in striking formwork and with curing.

4.7   POROUS NO-FINES CONCRETE

1. Porous no-fines concrete shall contain ordinary Portland cement and 20 mm single sized aggregate complying with BS 882, in a proportion of 1:10 by mass.

2. The concrete shall be mixed to a uniform colour and consistency with the addition of water sufficient only to coat all of the aggregate without forming excess grout.

3. The concrete shall not be mechanically vibrated or excessively worked when placed.

4.8   AIR-ENTRAINED CONCRETE

(i) Air entraining admixtures used in conjunction with pfa can give rise to very variable air content.

(ii) Compliance criteria for the air content of concrete are set out in Clause 3.6 of BS 5328: Part 4.

1. Where air-entrained concrete is required, it shall have an average air content by volume of the fresh concrete at the time of placing in accordance with Clause 4.3.3 of BS 5328: Part 1.

4.9   CHLORIDE CONTENT

(i) The limits for chloride ion content are consistent with Clause 6.2.5.2 of BS 8110: Part 1.

1. Calcium chloride or admixtures containing calcium chloride shall not be used in the production of reinforced concrete or concrete which is to contain embedded metal.

2. Steam-cured concrete shall not contain chloride ions, derived from all its constituents, in excess of 0.1% by mass of its cementitious content. The percentage for all other concrete containing embedded metal in the final work shall not exceed the following:

Portland cement concrete, rapid hardening Portland cement concrete, or combinations with ggbs or pfa	0.4, save that the proportion may be up to 0.5 in not more than 5% of the test results.
Concrete made with sulfate-resisting or supersulfated cement	0.2

Assessment of compliance shall be in accordance with Clause 3.7 of BS 5328: Part 4 and shall be based on measured values of chloride ion content.

4.10   ADJUSTMENTS TO DESIGNED MIX PROPORTIONS

1. During production of Designed mix concrete, the Contractor shall adjust mix proportions within the limits prescribed in BS 5328: Part 3 to achieve the required strength and workability and shall provide the details required by Clause 3.2.3 of BS 5328: Part 3 to the Engineer.

4.11   WORKABILITY

1. Workability of fresh concrete shall be such that the concrete can be handled and placed without segregation and, after compaction, can completely fill the formwork and surround all reinforcement and ducts.

2. The quantity of water used shall not exceed that required to produce a concrete with appropriate workability to be placed and compacted in the required location.

(i) Any requirements for placing concrete in special sequence, e.g. by alternate bay construction, should be described in the Contract.

4.12   TRANSPORTING, PLACING AND COMPACTING

1. Concrete shall be transported from the mixer in accordance with Clause 4.10 of BS 5328: Part 3 and placed in the Works as rapidly as practicable by methods which will prevent the segregation or loss of any of the ingredients and will maintain the required workability. It shall be deposited as nearly as practicable in its final position and all equipment for transporting concrete shall be kept clean.

2. The Contractor shall give adequate notice to the Engineer of his intention to commence concreting.

3. Concrete shall be thoroughly compacted in its final position within 30 minutes of discharge from the mixer, unless carried in purpose-made agitators operating continuously, when the time shall be within 2 hours of the introduction of the cement to the mix and within 30 minutes of the discharge from the agitator.

4. The plant used for compaction shall be operated continuously during the placing of each batch of concrete until the expulsion of air has virtually ceased, and in a manner which does not promote segregation of the ingredients.

5. Whenever vibration has to be applied externally, the design of formwork and disposition of vibrators shall be such as to ensure efficient compaction and to avoid surface blemishes.

4.13   CONCRETING IN COLD WEATHER

1. Concreting at ambient temperatures below $2^{\circ}C$ may be carried out only if the following conditions are met:

(a)   the aggregates and water used in the mix shall be free from snow, ice and frost,

(b)   before placing concrete, the formwork, reinforcement and any surface with which the fresh concrete will be in contact shall be free from snow, ice and frost and shall be at a temperature above $0^{\circ}C$,

(c)   the initial temperature of the concrete at the time of placing shall be at least $5^{\circ}C$,

(d)   the temperature at the surface of the concrete shall be maintained at not less than $5^{\circ}C$ at any point until the concrete reaches a strength of 5 N/mm^2, as confirmed by tests on cubes matured under similar conditions, and

(e)   temperatures at the surface of the concrete shall be measured where the lowest temperature is expected.

2. The Contractor shall take precautions to prevent the temperature of any concrete falling to $0^{\circ}C$ during the first five days after placing.

4.14   CONCRETE TEMPERATURE

1. The resultant temperature of the combined materials in any batch of concrete at the point and time of delivery to the Works shall not exceed $6^{\circ}C$ above the prevailing shade temperature, when the latter is over $21^{\circ}C$.

2. The Contractor shall not permit any cement to come into contact with water at a temperature greater than $60^{\circ}C$.

3. Where the temperature of the fresh concrete is likely to exceed $32^{\circ}C$, concreting shall not be permitted unless measures are taken to keep the temperature below that level.

(i) Consideration may have to be given to measures to prevent thermal cracking where a temperature differential in excess of $20^{o}C$ is likely to occur, for example by extending striking times for the formwork.

(ii) The table in Clause 4.15.1 is taken from Table 6.5 of BS 8110: Part 1 and the ambient conditions therefore have the following meanings:

good: damp and protected (relative humidity greater than 80%; protected from sun and wind).

average: intermediate between good and poor.

poor: dry or unprotected (relative humidity less than 50%; not protected from sun and wind).

4.15 CURING

1. Concrete shall be cured for a period not less than that given in the following table, by methods that shall ensure that cracking, distortion and efflorescence are minimised:

Type of cement	Ambient conditions after casting	Minimum period of curing and protection	
		$5^{o}C$ to $10^{o}C$	Above $10^{o}C$
BS 12 and BS 4027	Average	4 days	3 days
	Poor	6 days	4 days
All except BS 12 and BS 4027 and all with pfa or ggbs	Average		
	Poor	10 days	7 days
All	Good	No special requirements	

2. In cold weather, when the temperature of freshly placed concrete may approach $0^{o}C$, water curing shall not be employed.

3. Components which are intended to have a similar exposed surface finish shall receive the same treatment.

4.16 RECORDS OF CONCRETING

1. The Contractor shall keep up to date records of the dates and times when concreting is carried out and of the weather and temperatures at those times. The records shall be available for inspection by the Engineer.

4.17 CONSTRUCTION OF FORMWORK

(i) BS 5975 gives recommendations as to standards of good practice in formwork construction.

(ii) The positioning and detailing of movement joints should be described in the Contract.

(iii) Any special conditions relating to the re-use of forms, insofar as the materials of construction and repairs between uses may affect the colour and surface finish of exposed surfaces, should be described in the Contract.

(iv) Any special requirements regarding chamfers to internal and external angles should be described in the Contract.

1. Formwork shall be sufficiently rigid and tight to prevent loss of mortar from the concrete and to maintain the correct position, shape and dimensions of the finished work. It shall be so constructed as to be removable from the cast concrete without shock or damage.

2. The forms shall be capable of producing a consistent quality of surface as described in the Contract.

3. Where holes are required in forms to accommodate projecting reinforcement, fixing devices or other built-in items, precautions shall be taken to prevent loss of mortar matrix.

4. Formwork shall give access for the preparation of joint surfaces before the concrete has hardened.

5. For the purposes of compliance with the provisions of Clause 4.19.3, the Contractor's method of constructing formwork shall allow for props to soffit forms to remain in position continuously for the period described.

4.18 CLEANING AND TREATMENT OF FORMS

1. The interiors of all forms shall be thoroughly cleaned out before any concrete is placed. The faces of the forms in contact with the concrete shall be clean and treated with a suitable release agent, where applicable.

2. Where a concrete surface is to be permanently exposed, only one release agent shall be used throughout the entire area. Release agents shall be applied evenly and contact with reinforcement and other embedded items avoided. Where the concrete surface is to receive an applied finish, care shall be taken to ensure the compatability of the release agent with the finish.

4.19 STRIKING OF FORMWORK

(i) As the removal of formwork is dependent upon the Contractor's method of working, the Engineer may wish to agree a formal procedure for determining striking times based on CIRIA Report R67 - Tables of Minimum Striking Times for Soffit and Vertical Formwork and Report R73-Formwork Striking Times - Methods of Assessment.

(ii) It should be noted that 11 hours at $15^{o}C$ is equivalent to:

8 hours at $20^{o}C$
15 hours at $10^{o}C$
24 hours at $5^{o}C$

8 hours at $15^{o}C$ is equivalent to
6 hours at $20^{o}C$
12 hours at $10^{o}C$
18 hours at $5^{o}C$

(iii) Any requirement for the control of thermal cracking should be described in the Contract.

1. Formwork shall be removed without shock to or disturbance of the concrete.

2. Formwork to vertical surfaces or sloping formwork not supporting concrete in flexure shall not be removed until, the concrete strength shall be sufficient to meet any wind loading upon the concrete likely to arise at the time when the formwork is removed; and

(a)   the concrete strength (as confirmed by tests in cubes cured under representative conditions) has reached 5 N/mm^2 or;

(b)   for concrete containing Portland cement only, in the absence of cube test results a minimum period shall have elapsed since the concrete was poured equivalent to 11 hours at 15°C for unsealed plywood forms, or 8 hours at 15°C for impermeable forms.

3. Formwork supporting concrete in flexure shall not be removed until:

(a) the concrete strength (as confirmed by tests on cubes cured under representative conditions) has reached 10 N/mm^2, or twice the stress to which the concrete will then be subjected, whichever is the greater or;

(b) for concretes containing Portland cement only, in the absence of cube test results or any formal procedure agreed in writing with the Engineer, the periods before striking calculated from the relevant formula given in the following table shall be used:

Type of formwork	Period calculated for mean ambient temperature(t) between 0°C and 25°C using formulae below
Soffit forms to slabs and beams	$\dfrac{100}{t + 10}$ days
Props to slabs and beams	$\dfrac{250}{t + 10}$ days

4. The Contractor shall give adequate notice to the Engineer of his intention to strike formwork.

4.20 SLOPING FORMWORK

(i) Any requirement for top formwork at slopes flatter than 30° to the horizontal should be described in the Contract.

1. Top formwork shall be provided to slopes 30° or more from the horizontal.

4.21 CUTTING AND BENDING OF REINFORCEMENT

1. Cutting and bending of reinforcement shall be in accordance with BS 4466 and shall be done without the application of heat and in a temperature of not less than 5°C. Bends shall have a substantially constant curvature.

2. Reinforcement shall not be straightened or rebent without the approval of the Engineer. If permission is given to bend projecting reinforcement, care shall be taken not to damage the concrete and to ensure that the radius is not less than the minimum specified in BS 4466.

4.22 FIXING OF REINFORCEMENT

1. Reinforcement shall be firmly supported in position and secured against displacement.

2. Non-structural connections for the positioning of reinforcement shall be made with tying wire or other fixing devices. Precautions shall be taken to ensure that projecting ends of ties or clips do not encroach into the concrete cover.

3. The concrete cover shall be not less than the required cover minus 5 mm and, where reinforcement is located in relation to only one face of a member, not more than the required cover plus:

5 mm for bars up to and including 12 mm size
10 mm for bars over 12 mm up to and including 25 mm size
15 mm for bars over 25 mm size.

(i) Any protection required for steel left projecting should be described in the Contract.

4.23 SURFACE CONDITION OF REINFORCEMENT

1. Concrete shall not be placed until reinforcement is free from any substance which might adversely affect the steel or concrete chemically or reduce the bond.

4.24 LAPS AND JOINTS

1. Laps and joints in reinforcement shall be made only at the positions described in the Contract or as agreed by the Engineer.

4.25 WELDING OF REINFORCEMENT

1. Reinforcement shall not be welded on Site except where described in or permitted under the Contract. All welding procedures shall be subject to the prior approval of the Engineer in writing.

4.26 BUILT-IN ITEMS

1. Where pipes, sleeves, water bars or other items are built into concrete, they shall be rigidly secured in position to prevent movement and shall be free from external coatings which might reduce the bond. The Contractor shall take precautions to prevent the formation or air pockets, voids or other defects whilst the concrete is being placed.

(i) The positioning and form of construction joints in structures designed to retain an aqueous liquid should be with a view to the control of cracking. See BS 8007, Section 5.

4.27   CONSTRUCTION JOINTS

1. Except where construction joints in concrete are described in the contract, the Contractor shall obtain the Engineer's approval to the positions and details of such joints before any work is commenced.

2. Joint lines shall be arranged to coincide wherever possible with features of the finished work.

3. Concreting shall be carried out continuously up to construction joints.

4. Concrete shall not be allowed to taper off to a thickness of less than 50 mm. Vertical joints shall be formed against a stop board suitably notched to accommodate the reinforcement. The top surface of each lift of concrete shall be straight and level unless described otherwise in the Contract.

5. Where a kicker is used, it shall be at least 70 mm high and shall be incorporated with the previous concrete.

6. The surface of any concrete against which new concrete is to be cast shall be free from laitance and shall be roughened to the extent that the large aggregate is exposed but not disturbed. The joint surface shall be cleaned immediately before the fresh concrete is placed against it.

7. Where practicable, such preparation of joints shall be carried out when the concrete has set but not hardened.

(i) The three finishes are intended to be applied as follows:

4.28   SURFACE FINISHES PRODUCED WITHOUT FORMWORK

Screeded Finish

Screeded - surfaces to receive further treatment or of no visual merit, or expressly suitable to their function with the workmanship as specified.

1. The concrete shall be levelled and screeded to produce a uniform plain or ridged surface as required. No further work shall be applied to the surface unless it is a first stage for a Wood Float or Steel Trowel Finish.

Wood Float Finish

Wood Float - surfaces where a reasonably regular finish is required, but appearance is not of prime importance.

2. The Screeded Finish shall be wood floated under light pressure to eliminate surface irregularities.

Steel Trowel Finish

Steel Trowel - surfaces where appearance is important.

Any other required finish should be described in the Contract.

3. When the moisture film has disappeared and the concrete has hardened sufficiently to prevent laitance from being worked to the surface, the surface to the Wood Float Finish shall be steel-trowelled under firm pressure to produce a dense, smooth, uniform surface free from trowel marks.

4. Where the type of finish is not given it shall be Wood Float Finish.

4.29 SURFACE FINISHES PRODUCED WITH FORMWORK

(i) The three types of Surface Finish are consistent with Types A, B and C in Clause 6.10.3 of BS 8110: Part 1 and are intended to be applied as follows:

A Rough - surfaces next to earth, or to receive further treatment, or of no visual merit, or expressly suitable to their function with workmanship as specified.

Rough Finish

1. This finish shall be obtained by the use of moulds or properly designed forms of closely-jointed sawn boards. The surface shall be free from substantial voids, honeycombing or other large blemishes.

B Fair - surfaces required for serviceability and structural soundness and which are not visually important.

Fair Finish

2. This finish shall be obtained from forms designed to produce a hard smooth surface with true, clean arrises. Only very minor surface blemishes shall be permitted and there shall be no staining or discolouration. Any projections shall be removed and the surface made good.

C Fair Worked - aqueous liquid retaining faces and other surfaces to good quality concrete, required for serviceability, structural soundness and appearance.

Fair Worked Finish

3. This finish shall be obtained by first producing a Fair Finish and then filling all surface blemishes with a fresh, specially prepared cement and fine aggregate paste whilst the concrete is still green where possible. After the concrete has been properly cured, the faces shall be rubbed down, if required, to produce a smooth and even surface. If the surface is to be exposed in the final work, every effort shall be made to match the colour of the concrete.

(ii) If test panels are required, these should be described in the Contract.

4.30 HIGH STRENGTH CONCRETE TOPPING

1. High strength concrete topping (granolithic finish) shall be provided, laid and finished in accordance with the relevant provisions of BS 8204: Part 2.

4.31 TIE BOLTS FOR FORMWORK

1. Only tie bolts which avoid embedding any metal parts permanently within 50 mm of the concrete surface shall be permitted. Voids remaining after the removal of all or part of each tie bolt shall be filled flush with the surrounding concrete using a freshly prepared cement and fine aggregate paste. In the case of structures designed to retain an aqueous liquid, the Contractor shall ensure that the measures adopted shall not impair the watertightness of the structure.

4.32 MARKING OF PRECAST CONCRETE COMPONENTS

1. Where appropriate, indelible identification and orientation marks shall be put on all precast concrete components in such a position that the marks shall not show or be exposed in the finished work.

4.33 TOLERANCE FOR CONCRETE SURFACES

(i) The table in Clause 4.33 applies to general concrete structures. Where more stringent tolerances are required, these should be described in the Contract (e.g. measuring flumes or areas where plant is to be installed).

1. Concrete surfaces in the final work shall have no abrupt irregularities to an extent observable by eye. Subject to retaining the required concrete cover to reinforcement, other deviations from the surfaces described in the Contract shall be no more than the following permissible amounts:

Type of Finish	Deviation from line, level, verticality, cross sectional dimension or length (mm)
Screeded or Rough	10
Any other	5

SECTION 5

CONSTRUCTION OF PIPELINES, TUNNELS AND ANCILLARY WORKS

(i) The following publications give recommendations on standards of good practice for the installation of pipelines on land:

BS8010
Part 1   Pipelines on land:
*   General*
Section 2.1   Ductile Iron
Section 2.3   Asbestos-cement
Section 2.4   Prestressed Concrete
*   pressure pipelines*
Section 2.5   GRP
Section 2.7   Precast Concrete
Section 2.8   Steel for Oil and Gas
BS 5927   Laying of Asbestos-
*   Cement Pipelines*

BS 5955: Part 6 Plastics Pipework
*   (Gravity)*

BS 8005 Sewerage: Part 1

'Principles of Laying Sewers', is a guide to good site practice available from WSA.

CP 312 Plastics pipework (thermoplastics materials): Parts 1, 2 and 3.

(ii) For handling of pipes, see Clause 2.3.

(iii) For minimum clearances to pipes in rock trenches, see Clause 3.1.

(iv) For details of marker tapes see Clause 2.42.

5.1   PIPELAYING GENERALLY

1. Where socketed pipes are required to be laid on a granular or sand bed, or directly on a trench bottom, joint holes shall be formed in the bedding material or excavated Final Surface to ensure that each pipe is uniformly supported throughout the length of its barrel and to enable the joint to made.

2. Pipe shall be laid on setting blocks only where a concrete bed or cradle is used.

3. Where pipes are required to be bedded directly on the trench bottom, the Final Surface shall be trimmed and levelled to provide even bedding of the pipeline and shall be free from all extraneous matter that may damage the pipe, pipe coating, or sleeving.

4. No protective cap, disc or other appliance on the end of a pipe or fitting shall be removed permanently until the pipe or fitting which it protects is about to be jointed. Pipes and fittings, including any lining or sheathing, shall be examined for damage and the joint surfaces and components shall be cleaned immediately before laying.

5. Suitable measures shall be taken to prevent soil or other material from entering pipes, and to anchor each pipe to prevent flotation or other movement before the Works are complete.

6. Where pipeline marker tape is specified, it shall be laid between 100 mm and 300 mm above the pipe. Where a tracer system is specified it shall be continuous and adequately secured to valves and fittings.

(i) When puddled clay stanks are required, these should be described in the Contract.

5.2   PIPE BEDDING

1. Bedding for pipes shall be constructed by spreading and compacting granular bedding material over the full width of the pipe trench. After the pipes have been laid, additional material shall, if required, be placed and compacted equally on each side of the pipes, and where practicable, this shall be done in sequence with the removal of the trench supports.

5.3   CONCRETE PROTECTION TO PIPES

1. Pipes to be bedded on or cradled with concrete shall be supported on precast concrete setting blocks, the top face of each block being covered with two layers of compressible packing in accordance with Clause 2.52.

2. Concrete provided as a protection to pipes shall be Grade C20, placed to the required depth in one operation.

3. Where pipes with flexible joints are used, concrete protection shall be interrupted over its full cross-section at each pipe joint by a shaped compressible filler in accordance with Clause 2.52.

4. Rapid hardening cement shall not be used in concrete for the protection of plastics pipe.

5. Plastics pipes shall be wrapped with a layer of plastic sheeting complying with Clause 2.26.1 before being surrounded by concrete.

5.4   COMPLETION OF PIPE SURROUND

1. After completion of the relevant operations in Clauses 5.1, 5.2 and 5.3, fill material shall, where required, be placed and compacted over the full width of the trench in layers not exceeding 150 mm before compaction, to a finished thickness of 250 mm above the crown of the pipes.

2. Subsequent filling shall then be carried out as specified in Clause 3.7.

5.5   PIPELAYING IN HEADINGS

(i) See also Clauses 3.1, 5.1 and 5.3.

1. Pipes to be laid in headings shall be supplied in lengths suitable for handling, jointing and packing within the working space available.

2. Headings shall be driven from shaft to shaft or in such other lengths as may be described in the Contract before any pipelaying is commenced.

3. After pipelaying, headings shall be packed solid with Grade C20 concrete so as to fill all voids. Where manual packing is employed, each pipe shall be surrounded before laying and jointing the next pipe.

4. Where grouting of headings is described in the Contract, grouting pipes shall be left in the top of the heading projecting behind each head tree and the whole grouted solid with grout Class G1. Grouting shall be carried out at the end of each shift or after three settings have been packed, whichever is the shorter interval.

5.6   THRUST BLOCKS

(i) Thrust blocks should either be described in the Contract or constructed in accordance with the Engineer's instructions on Site.

1. Except where welded steel pipelines or self anchoring joints are used thrusts from bends and branches in pressure pipelines shall be resisted by concrete thrust blocks cast in contact with undisturbed ground.

2. Any additional excavation required to accommodate thrust blocks shall be carried out after the bend or branch is in position and the thrust face shall be trimmed back to remove all loose or weathered material immediately prior to concreting.

3. Thrust blocks shall be allowed to develop adequate strength before any internal pressure is applied to the pipeline.

4. Rapid hardening cement shall not be used in concrete for thrust blocks to plastics pipe.

5. Plastics pipes shall be wrapped with a layer of plastic sheeting complying with Clause 2.26.1 before being surrounded by concrete.

(i) Proprietary joints are required to be made in accordance with the manufacturers' instructions. See Clause 2.3.

(ii) Any special requirements for filling the joint annulus should be described in the Contract.

(iii) The remaining flexibility is required for any subsequent settlement or ground movement.

5.7 PIPE JOINTING GENERALLY

1. Pipe jointing surfaces and components shall be kept clean and free from extraneous matter until the joints have been made or assembled. Care shall be taken to ensure that there is no ingress of grout or other extraneous material into the joint annulus after the joint has been made.

2. Where pipes with flexible joints are required to be laid to curves, the deflection at any joint as laid shall not exceed three quarters of the maximum deflection recommended by the manufacturer.

(i) Different types of PE 'soften' at different temperatures and when soft have different viscosities which may impair the jointing process.

(ii) Joints in HDPE and MDPE should be made in accordance with the manufacturers' instructions. See Clause 2.3.

(iii) Any requirement for weld tests should be described in the Contract.

(iv) IGN No. 4-31-01 deals with PVC-U pipe jointing.

5.8 WELDED JOINTS IN PLASTICS PIPES

1. Fusion welded joints in high density and medium density polyethylene pipes shall be made only between pipes having the same physical characteristics. Joints between pipes from different manufacturers shall only be made with the specific approval of the Engineer.

2. Site fusion jointing shall be made in accordance with WIs No. 4-32-08.

3. When solvent welded PVC-U pipes are jointed outside the trench, they shall not be lowered into place until the period recommended by the manufacturer for complete setting of the joints has elapsed.

4. A pipe section containing a completed weld shall achieve the same strength characteristics as the parent pipe.

(i) Where the Contractor is not required to provide nuts, bolts, washers and/or jointing gaskets, this should be described in the Contract.

(ii) Any special requirements for the type of flange gasket should be described in the Contract. See also Clause 2.48.

5.9 FLANGED JOINTS

1. Flanges shall be properly aligned before any bolts are tightened.

2. Jointing compounds shall not be used when making flanged joints, except that, to facilitate the making of vertical joints, gaskets may be secured temporarily to one flange face by a minimum quantity of clear rubber solution. Bolt threads shall be treated with graphite paste and the nuts tightened evenly in diametrically opposite pairs.

(i) Any required jointing material (mastic or cement mortar) should be described in the Contract.

5.10 OGEE JOINTS

1. Ogee joints shall be so made that the required jointing material fills the joint cavity. Any surplus jointing material extruded inside the barrel shall be trimmed off and, where practicable, pointed on completion.

(i) For guidance on welding reference may be made to:
BS 534, BS 2971, BS 3601, BS 4515, BS 5135, BS 8010: Section 2.8.

(ii) The types of welded joint should be described in the Contract.

5.11 WELDED JOINTS IN STEEL PIPES

1. The process of welding steel pipelines shall be in accordance with BS 4515.

2. The ends of pipes shall be cut and prepared, and be free from fins, planar defects, tears and other surface defects, prior to welding. Cleaning to base metal shall extend for at least 25mm from the end of the pipe on both internal and external faces.

3. The alignment of abutting pipe ends shall be such as to minimise the internal offset between surfaces.

(iii) The frequency and type of testing should be described in the Contract.

4. The Contractor shall submit details of the proposed welding and welding repair procedures, before production welding begins, and test welds using these procedures shall be made by the Contractor under simulated site conditions.

5. Welders shall only make welds for which they are approved.

6. Joints shall be tested using non-destructive techniques, unless it is necessary to use destructive testing to achieve adequate interpretation.

5.12   CEMENT MORTAR JOINTS

(i) This Clause is intended to refer only to pipes cut on Site.

1. In making yarn and mortar joints for pipes or fittings, the spigot shall be entered into the socket of the last pipe laid until it bears on the back face of the socket, and it shall be centred in the socket. Two turns of tarred yarn shall then be caulked into the back of the socket and Class M1 cement mortar shall be pressed into the joint to fill the socket and shall be bevelled off at 45° from the outside edge of the socket.

5.13   RUN LEAD JOINTS

1. Run lead joints shall be made by forcing home strands of white sterilised jute piping yarn, to the back of the socket cavity leaving a space of 75 mm (60 mm for pipes of 300 mm nominal bore and below) measured from the socket face. The socket face shall then be encircled by a suitable clip or gasket and the joint cavity filled with molten lead poured in one running. After cooling, the lead shall be set up and neatly finished with the face of the lead 2 mm back from the socket face. In the case of pipes over 750 mm diameter, the socket and spigot shall be heated before the joint is run.

5.14   PROTECTION OF FERROUS PIPES, JOINTS AND FITTINGS

(i) For application of protection see Clause 2.3.2.

(ii) Any limitation on the type of external or internal protection required should be described in the Contract.

1. Ferrous pipes, joints and fittings shall be cleaned and all loose rust removed before protection is applied.

2. External protection for bolted joints and fittings shall comprise:

P1   The application of mastic paste in sufficient quantity to cover all protruding edges, bolt heads and sharp edges of flanges, to give a smooth external profile. The joint or fitting shall be wrapped with two separate applications of protective tape wound spirally with a minimum half width overlap. The taping shall extend along 150 mm of the barrel of the pipe on each side of the joint or fitting.

or

P2   The application of a self-adhesive rubber-based cold-applied tape wrap combined with a thick PVC backing. Where bolt heads, flanges and other projections arise a moulding putty shall be used to give a smooth external profile. The joint or fitting shall be wrapped with two separate applications of protective tape wrap wound spirally with minimum of half width overlap, The tape shall extend along 150 mm of the barrel of the pipe on each side of joint or fitting.

or

P3   The application of heat shrink sleeves.

3. External protection for ductile iron pipes shall comprise:

P4   The covering of the pipes with lay flat polythene sleeving securely held in place with adhesive tape at pipe joints and intermediate positions.

or

P5   The factory application of plastic sleeving. The protection of joints and repairs to any damage shall be in accordance with Clause 2.3.2.

or

P6   The factory application of plastic tape. The protection of joints and repairs to any damage shall be in accordance with Clause 2.3.2.

or

(iii) The type of external protection required should be described in the Contract.

P7   Painting the external surface as described in the Contract.

4. Completion of internal and external protection of steel pipes shall be provided where pipes have a bituminous, epoxy or any other type of proprietary protective coating in which a gap has been left for the joint to be made. The joint and any damage to the protective coating shall be made good.

(iv) For guidance on cathodic protection see BS 7361: Part 1 and 'Guides to practice in corrosion control - No 9, Cathodic Protection' Published by the National Corrosion Service of the National Physical Laboratory.

5. Cathodic protection of pipes, joints and fittings shall comprise either impressed current or sacrificial anode.

(v) Any requirements for the design of the cathodic protection should be described in the Contract.

5.15   CUTTING PIPES

(i) Particular requirements for welded steel pipes are given in Clause 5.11.

1. Pipes shall be cut by a method which provides a clean square profile, without splitting or fracturing the pipe wall, and which causes minimal damage to any protective coating. Where necessary, the cut ends of pipes shall be formed to the tapers and chamfers suitable for the type of joint to be used and any protective coatings shall be made good, and the ends sealed.

2. Where ductile pipes are to be cut to form non-standard lengths, the Contractor shall comply with the manufacturer's recommendations in respect of ovality correction and tolerances to the cut spigot end.

5.16   PRECAST CONCRETE MANHOLES

(i) The type of jointing material should be described in the Contract.

1. Precast concrete chamber and shaft sections shall be constructed with step irons, ladders or slabs aligned correctly.

2. Joints shall be made so that the required jointing material fills the joint cavity. Any surplus jointing material extruded inside the chamber or shaft shall be trimmed off and joints shall be pointed on completion.

3. Where manholes are to have a concrete surround, the concrete shall be Grade C20 and the height of each concrete pour shall not exceed 2 m. Each construction joint shall break joint with that of the chamber or shaft sections by a least 150 mm.

5.17 PRECAST CONCRETE SEGMENTAL MANHOLES

1. Precast concrete segmental manholes shall be constructed in accordance with the relevant provisions of Clauses 5.26 to 5.28 and 5.30 to 5.36.

5.18 BRICK AND IN-SITU CONCRETE MANHOLES AND CHAMBERS

1. Manholes and chambers constructed in brickwork or in-situ concrete shall comply with the relevant provisions of Sections 4 and 6 respectively.

5.19 INVERTS AND BENCHING

(i) The benching material and surface finish should be described in the Contract.

(ii) The Surface Finishes referred to are specified in Clauses 4.28 and 4.29.

1. Manhole inverts and benchings shall be formed of the materials described in the Contract and where there is no change of diameter, the invert shall follow the same gradient as the outgoing sewer.

2. Where inverts and benchings are to be formed of in-situ concrete or high strength concrete topping (granolithic finish), the relevant provisions of Section 4 shall apply.

3. Where a high strength concrete topping (granolithic finish) is required, the invert and benching shall be formed in Grade C20 concrete with a Screeded Finish or Rough Finish as required, and the concrete topping shall be applied as soon as practicable thereafter.

4. Where the finished surface is to be in-situ concrete, the concrete shall be Grade C20 with a Steel Trowel or Fair Worked Finish as required.

5. Where the inverts of both manhole and sewer are constructed of brickwork, there shall be no break in bond between the two.

5.20 PIPES AND JOINTS ADJACENT TO STRUCTURES

(i) The requirements for rocker pipes are consistent with BS 8005: Part 1 which does not recommend them for pipes above 750 mm nominal bore.

1. Except where the construction is by tunnelling, heading or pipe jacking, a flexible joint shall be provided as close as is feasible to the outside face of any structure into which the pipe is built, compatible with the satisfactory completion and subsequent movement of the joint.

2. The length of the next pipe (rocker pipe) away from the structure shall be in the range 0.5 m to 0.75 m for pipes up to 450 mm nominal bore and shall not exceed 1 m for pipes up to 750 mm nominal bore.

3. A pipeline may, where practicable, be laid through a manhole and the crown cut out to the half diameter, provided flexible joints are situated on each side, no further than 600 mm from the inner face of the manhole wall, and that adjacent pipes comply with Sub-clause 2 of this Clause.

5.21 WATERTIGHTNESS OF MANHOLES AND CHAMBERS

(i) See also Clause 7.8.

1. Manholes and chambers shall be substantially watertight, with no identifiable flow of water penetrating the Permanent Works.

5.22 SETTING MANHOLE COVERS AND FRAMES

(i) This clause covers the normal case. If bedding of frames on epoxy resin or haunching in concrete (instead of mortar) is required, this should be described in the Contract.

1. Manhole frames shall be set to the required level on Class B engineering brickwork, or on precast concrete cover frame seating rings, as described in the Contract. The frames shall be set to level, bedded and haunched over the base and sides of the frame in Class M1 mortar.

5.23 CONNECTIONS TO EXISTING SEWERS

1. Pipe saddles for concrete or clay sewers shall be bedded in Class M1 mortar and a mortar fillet formed to give a cover of at least 50 mm to the base of the saddle. Pipe saddles for asbestos-cement sewer pipes shall be formed from asbestos-cement and fixed with an epoxy resin adhesive.

2. Pipe saddles for PVC-U pipes shall be purpose made from PVC-U and shall either be of a mechanical clip-on type or shall be fixed with an appropriate solvent cement.

3. Where an appropriate saddle or junction unit is unobtainable a connection to an existing sewer may be made with a pipe cut to give an oblique junction, so that the discharge is in the direction of flow in the main sewer. The connecting pipes shall be of such a length that the socket of the cut pipe rests on the outside barrel of the sewer with no projection inside the main sewer. The pipe joint shall then be pointed in Class M1 mortar externally, and internally where practicable. Alternatively, purpose made junctions may be used by cutting out sections of pipe, fitting a junction and securing with repair couplings.

4. The ends of connections and pipes not required for immediate use shall be closed with purpose made stoppers, discs or joinders. The position of all junctions shall be recorded by the Contractor by measurement from the manhole immediately downstream and notified to the Engineer before backfilling is commenced.

5.24 SEWERS AND MANHOLES TO BE ABANDONED

(i) The material required for filling should be described in the Contract.

1. Where sewers are to be abandoned and filled by grouting, the lowest point of the abandoned length shall be suitably sealed, and the filling operation shall commence from that point and continue progressively so as to fill all voids completely.

(ii) Any requirement for clearing sewers prior to filling should be described in the Contract.

2. The shafts of manholes on abandoned sewers shall be broken down to a level 1 m below finished ground level and the remaining void filled as described in the Contract.

5.25 PIPE JACKING

1. Excavation for pipe jacking shall be undertaken from within a shield equipped with steering jacks for adjusting the alignment. Face boards shall be available for boarding up the exposed excavation.

(i) Clause 15 of the Sixth Edition deals generally with super-intendence; this clause ensures continuous superintendence during jacking operations.

2. The Contractor shall provide such continuous superintendence as is necessary to maintain the line and level during jacking of the pipe.

3. The Contractor shall limit the jacking load applied to the pipeline such that damage to the pipes is avoided and in this connection he shall be responsible for deciding whether an intermediate jacking station is needed.

(ii) Advice on intermediate jacking stations is given in 'A Guide to Pipe Jacking Design' published by the Pipe Jacking Association in June 1981.

4. The jacking load shall be transferred to the pipes through a thrust ring, which shall be sufficiently rigid to ensure even distribution of the load.

5. The pipe manufacturer's described permitted draw or angular deflection in relation to Table 6 of BS 5911: Part 120 shall not be exceeded at any individual joint.

(iii) Collars fabricated from weldable structural steel may be susceptible to corrosion from the ground, ground water or the effluent carried. If corrosion can be expected, the design of joint should provide for a secondary sealing gasket to be applied on Site.

6. The Contractor shall maintain up to date Site records of jacking loads and line and level measurements.

7. All lifting holes and grouting holes shall be sealed with Class M1 mortar.

8. Unless otherwise required by the Contract joint packing material designed to distribute the jacking load evenly shall be inserted at and between the pipe ends and at any intermediate jacking stations.

9. Where grouting is required this shall be carried out in accordance with Clause 5.31, after the pipes have been jacked into their final position.

5.26   SHAFTS

(i)   Any   special   requirements relating   to   protection   should   be described in the Contract.

(ii) Special clauses will be required for other types of shaft sinking.

1. The Contractor shall provide temporary ladders to all shafts, with landings at intervals not exceeding 6 m. Protection shall be so provided that neither the ladders, landings, supporting structures nor persons using them are subject to the risk of damage or injury by the passage of skips and/or materials in the shaft.

2. Segments used in shafts shall be so erected as to break vertical joint except in any rings required to be broken out.

3. Where shafts are constructed by underpinning and lined with segments, they shall be grouted up at least once per shift.

4. After any primary lining is complete and before any openings are made at or near the foot, the excavation for the base of the shaft shall be taken out and the base concreted.

5.27   OPENINGS IN SHAFTS AND TUNNELS

(i) Although the Engineer may call for details under Clause 14 (6) of the Sixth Edition, this clause is included to make the submission of details obligatory.

(ii) The Contract should describe any limitations which the design of the tunnel or shaft will impose on temporary openings.

1. The Contractor shall supply to the Engineer drawings showing his proposals for forming openings in shafts and tunnels. These drawings shall include details of temporary supports to the lining and to the ground.

2. Openings in shafts and tunnels shall only be made after the segments have been grouted.

5.28   SEGMENTAL SHAFT AND TUNNEL LININGS

1. Before each ring of any segmental lining is erected, any loose material or other obstructions shall be removed from any exposed Final Surface.

2. Segments shall be erected and assembled in-situ ring by ring and joint faces shall be clean on erection. The lining shall be built as soon as possible after the ground has been cut.

5.29   UNBOLTED CONCRETE TUNNEL SEGMENTS

(i)   Requirements   for   any circumferential pre-stress should be described in the Contract.

1. The shape of unbolted concrete segmental tunnels shall be maintained within tolerance after erection, until the segments have been stabilised by grout or other means.

2. Where a circumferential pre-stress is applied, the force shall be such that the whole of the concrete lining is expanded tight against the surrounding ground. An approved graphite compound shall be applied to the wedge faces of segments immediately prior to expanding the ring.

3. Where wedge block segments are specified, the excavated tunnel periphery shall be lubricated to reduce skin friction.

4. Where key segments are shorter than other segments comprising the ring, the pockets formed shall be filled with Grade C20 concrete.

(i) Any requirement relating to rolling of segments should be described in the Contract.

(ii) Any requirement for bituminous jointing strips in circumferential joints should be described in the Contract.

5.30 BOLTED CONCRETE SEGMENTAL LININGS

1. Segmental joints to bolted concrete tunnel and shaft linings shall be trued and longitudinal joint bolts tightened before the final tightening of the circumferential joint bolts connecting the ring to the adjacent ring.

2. Bituminous jointing strip shall be provided to longitudinal joints.

3. Packings shall be inserted in the joints of the lining at the time of erection, as required, to maintain correct shape, line and level.

4. Two grummets shall be threaded on each bolt to be grummetted, at the time any bolted segment is erected. One grummet shall be placed under the washer at the head of the bolt and the other under the washer at the nut.

(i) Any requirements for high pressure grouting should be described in the Contract.

(ii) Any locations where it is required to grout more frequently than once per shift should be described in the Contract.

5. 31 GROUTING OF SEGMENTS

1. Segmental shaft and tunnel linings shall be grouted by forcing the required grout through the grouting holes in the segments, so that all interstices around the outside of the segments are filled. Adequate venting shall be provided to ensure that air is not trapped. Grouting shall closely follow the erection of rings and shall be undertaken at least once per shift.

2. Temporary hardwood plugs shall be inserted into grout holes after grouting; these shall be replaced by permanent plugs of material similar to that of the segments being grouted when it is evident to the Engineer that grouting has been effective.

3. Grout pipes shall be provided in head walls or ring walls and any void remaining after concreting shall be filled with the required grout.

(i) Material to be used for caulking should be described in the Contract.

(ii) The time when caulking is carried out may depend, inter alia, upon ground conditions and availability of the working area.

5.32 CAULKING

1. Caulking of segment joints in tunnels and shafts shall be carried out as late as practicable within the construction programme; the grooves shall be raked out and cleaned immediately before caulking.

2. Caulking of circumferential and longitudinal joints shall be bonded to form a homogeneous and continuous mass consolidated to fill the recess up to the inner surface of the segment or to the depths described in the Contract.

5.33 POINTING OF JOINTS

1. Where joints between segments are required to be pointed, they shall be raked out, cleaned, filled with a proprietary non-shrink cement mortar and pointed flush.

(i) See also Clause 7.8.

5.34 SHAFTS AND TUNNELS TO BE WATERTIGHT

1. Shafts and tunnels shall be substantially watertight, with no identifiable flow of water penetrating either the primary or secondary lining.

5.35 RECORDING INFORMATION

1. The Contractor shall keep records of the line, level and the diameter measured horizontally and vertically of any tunnel lining and shall give copies of these records daily to the Engineer. Similar records shall be kept and supplied for shafts and for pipe jacking.

(i) Where a tunnel is to have a secondary lining, it may be necessary to specify permissible deviations for the primary lining, having regard to the nature of the work.

(ii) Any requirements for more stringent tolerances should be described in the Contract.

(iii) Where a pipeline, shaft or tunnel is to be constructed in ground which is variable or unstable, it may be appropriate for a larger tolerance for line and level to be described in the Contract.

5.36   TOLERANCES FOR PIPELINES, SHAFTS AND TUNNELS

1. The position of the internal face of any pipeline, shaft or tunnel shall not deviate from that described in the Contract by more than the following permissible deviations:

Work category	Dimension or alignment	Possible deviation
Pipeline	Line and level	20 mm
Pipe jacking	Line	75 mm
	Level	50 mm
Shafts and chambers	Vertically	1 in 300
Shafts and tunnels	Finished diameter	1% but not exceeding 50 mm
Tunnels without secondary lining	Line (shield drive)	75 mm
	Line (hand drive)	50 mm
	Level (shield drive)	50 mm
	Level (hand drive)	25 mm
Tunnels with secondary lining	Line	20 mm
	Level	10 mm
Shaft, tunnel and sewer lining segments	Maximum lipping between edges of adjacent segments	5 mm

5.37   JUNCTIONS AND LATERALS ON SEWERS

1. Laterals shall be laid from the junctions to the boundary of the properties.

2. Junctions and laterals shall be effectively sealed with an end cap, the location of which shall be positively indicated.

5.38   MARKER AND INDICATOR POSTS

(i) Details and locations of marker, indicator posts and ground markers should be described in the Contract.

1. Marker posts shall be erected on the route of the pipeline and indicator posts at the location of valves and other fittings, where shown.

2. Permanent ground markers shall be constructed at locations shown. A schedule of co-ordinates of the ground markers shall be supplied to the Engineer on completion of the Contract.

SECTION 6

BUILDING WORKS

General Note

This Section is intended only for small scale building works to be carried out under the Sixth Edition of the ICE Conditions of Contract.

6.1 BRICKWORK AND BLOCKWORK GENERALLY

(i) Flush jointing is described in BS 5628: Part 3.

1. Brickwork and blockwork shall comply with the relevant provisions of BS 5628: Part 3.

(ii) Any requirement for rendering of manholes and chambers should be described in the Contract.

2. The moisture content of the bricks shall be adjusted so that excessive suction is not exerted on the mortar.

(iii) The bond should be described in the Contract.

3. Bricks in each course shall break joint correctly with the bricks underneath. The courses shall be laid parallel with joints of uniform thickness and shall be kept straight or regularly curved as required. Brickwork shall be gauged to rise 300 mm in four courses. Vertical joints shall be in alignment as required by the bond and shall have an average thickness of 10 mm. Bricks forming reveals and internal and external angles shall be selected for squareness and built plumb. Bricks with single frogs shall be laid frog upwards.

(iv) The required class of mortar and type of cement should be described in the Contract. See Clause 2.20.

4. Brickwork and blockwork shall rise uniformly; corners and other advanced work shall be raked back and not raised above the general level more than 1 m. No brickwork shall be carried up higher than 1.5 m in one day. No bats or broken bricks shall be incorporated in the work unless essential for bond. Where cut blocks are required, all cutting shall be carried out with a mechanical cutting disc.

5. Completed brickwork and blockwork shall be protected at all times from scaffold splash, mortar droppings, grout leakage from suspended slabs and the harmful effects of weather. Brickwork and blockwork shall be allowed to set thoroughly hard before cutting or chasing is carried out.

6.2 BRICKWORK AND BLOCKWORK, JOINTING AND POINTING

(i) The type of jointing and pointing should be described in the Contract.

1. Bricks and blocks shall be laid in mortar properly bedded and jointed and all joints filled with mortar at every course.

(ii) Provision should be made in the Contract for sample areas of different wall types and finishes.

2. Where the surface of walling does not provide an adequate key, the joints on faces of walls to be plastered shall be raked out 12 mm deep.

6.3 CAVITY WALLS

(i) Where the filling or semi-filling of cavities with insulating material is required it should be described in the Contract.

1. Cavity walls shall have 50 mm minimum width cavities and shall be built with wall ties uniformly spaced 450 mm apart vertically and 900 mm apart horizontally, staggered, and laid to fall outwards. Additional ties shall be used near the sides of all openings, one for each third course of bricks. Care shall be taken to keep the ties within the cavity free from mortar or mortar droppings and any mortar or debris collecting at the bottom of the cavity shall be cleaned out through temporary openings left for this purpose in the bottom courses.

2. Weepholes shall be provided by leaving open perpendicular joints at not greater than one metre intervals in the course immediately above the cavity tray, with not less than two weepholes over each opening.

6.4 DAMP PROOF COURSE

1. Construction of damp proof courses shall comply with the relevant provisions of, BS 5628: Part 3, BS 6576, BS 8102 and BS 8215.

6.5 CORBELLING

1. Oversail corbelling shall not exceed 30 mm on each course.

6.6 BONDING TO CONCRETE

1. Where brickwork or blockwork is to be bonded to concrete, this shall be achieved by means of metal ties evenly placed at three per square metre and brickwork and blockwork shall be brought up subsequent to the concrete.

6.7 UNDERPINNING

(i) Larger scale underpinning should be described in the Contract and may require the services of a specialist contractor.

1. Underpinning in brickwork shall be carried up to within one course of the underside of the existing structure and allowed to set. The remaining course shall be bedded in mortar and wedged with slate pieces tightly against the existing structure.

6.8 CENTERING AND LAGGING

1. Centering and lagging used for the construction of brickwork and blockwork shall remain in place for such time as is necessary for the brickwork and blockwork to develop sufficient strength to prevent sagging or cracking of joints.

6.9 BRICKLAYING AND BLOCKLAYING IN COLD WEATHER

1. Materials used in bricklaying and blocklaying shall be frost free and no bricks or blocks shall be laid when the ambient temperature is below $3^{\circ}C$, unless special precautions are taken. The Contractor shall ensure that any additive used in the mortar does not cause a variation in the colour of the joints. Completed work shall be protected adequately during cold weather.

6.10 PREPARATION FOR PLASTERING

1. Unless a bonding agent is used concrete ceilings, ceiling beams, columns and stanchions shall be dubbed out as necessary before plastering is commenced and the mix used for dubbing shall be similar to that used for first undercoating. The surface of in-situ concrete shall be cleaned of dust, loose particles and other matter. Surfaces shall be wetted immediately before plastering is commenced.

(i) The type of scrim material should be described in the Contract.

(ii) If joints are to be cut or covered as an alternative to scrim this should be described in the Contract.

2. Angles between walls and ceilings, vertical angles and joints between dissimilar solid backgrounds shall be reinforced with 90 mm wide scrim set in plaster and trowelled flat. All joints between plasterboards shall be similarly treated.

3. Expanded metal angle beads shall be provided at all external corners.

6.11 FIXING OF PLASTERBOARD

1. Plasterboard for ceilings shall be nailed to support at 150 mm centres with 40 mm sheradised plasterboard nails and fastened so that the joints are staggered. Noggins or other fixing surface shall be provided as necessary to ensure that edges of plasterboard are secured adequately. Ends of sheets shall be butted tightly and edges left with a gap not exceeding 5 mm.

2. Where sheeting has been cut, nails shall not be less than 18 mm from cut edges. Nails shall be driven well home with heads slightly below the surface, but shall not break the paper.

6.12 PLASTERING

1. Plastering shall normally be applied in two coats in accordance with the manufacturer's instructions and batches shall be used as soon as possible after water has been added. The total thickness of both coats shall be of the order of, but shall not exceed, 13 mm.

2. Where 3 coat work is described in the Contract, the thickness shall be of the order of, but shall not normally exceed, 18 mm.

3. The thickness of 2 coat work applied to concrete ceilings and soffits or plasterboard, shall not exceed 9 mm.

4. The thickness of finishing coats shall be of the order of 3 mm, except where board finished plaster is used, when the thickness shall be 5 mm and the work shall comply with the relevant provisions of BS 5492.

6.13 PLASTERING IN COLD WEATHER

1. When the ambient temperature is 5°C or less, the portion of the Works to be plastered shall be completely enclosed. The ambient temperature shall be raised and maintained above 5°C until the completion of plastering and hydration.

6.14 CONCRETE FLOOR FINISHES

(i) The type of finish from BS 8204: Part 2 should be described in the Contract.

1. Concrete floor finishes shall comply with the relevant provisions of BS 8204: Part 2.

6.15 FLOOR TILING

1. Floor tiling shall comply with the relevant provisions of BS 5385: Parts 3 and 5 for rigid tiling and BS 8203 for flexible tiling.

6.16 TERAZZO

1. Terazzo floor finishes shall comply with the relevant provisions of CP 204: Part 2, Section 3.

6.17 EXTERNAL RENDERING

1. External rendering shall comply with BS 5262 and shall be applied to a total thickness of not less than 20 mm. The mix for both coats shall be as for Class M4 mortar and the first coat shall be applied, levelled, scratched and left to dry for not less than 3 days in warm weather and not less than 7 days in cold or wet weather. The suction of the surface of the first coat shall be adjusted as necessary by wetting before applying the second coat which shall be coloured as directed, levelled and lightly trowelled with a wooden trowel.

6.18 WALL TILING

1. Wall tiling shall comply with the relevant provisions of BS 5385: Parts 1, 2 and 4.

6.19 CARPENTRY AND JOINERY

1. Wherever possible, cutting and shaping of all timber shall be completed before preservative treatment is carried out. Where any cutting or shaping has to be carried out after treatment, the cut or worked surfaces shall be given 2 coats of the preservative. After treatment, timber shall be thoroughly dried out before use.

2. The whole of the joinery shall be cut and framed together as soon as possible after the commencement of the work. Workmanship shall comply with the relevant provisions of BS 1186: Part 2 and BS 6446. Except where work is described in the Contract as being to finished sizes, 3 mm shall be allowed for each wrot face. Frames, casings and other joinery fittings shall be secured to hardwood fixing slips built in for the purpose. Where hardwood fixing slips have not been provided, receiving surfaces shall be plugged with hardwood plugs or approved proprietary type plugs.

3. Manufactured units to be painted shall be primed at the place of manufacture.

6.20   STRUCTURAL STEELWORK

1. All steelwork shall be Grade 43A to BS 4360.

2. All members shall be cut to length by cold sawing.

3. Where a structural member is supported on masonry or brickwork, the minimum length of bearing shall be 100 mm.

(i) This clause is intended to apply to minor structural steel members.

(ii) End connection, baseplates and other design requirements should be described in the Contract.

(iii) Where steelwork is to be galvanised it should be described in the Contract.

6.21   ROOFS

1. Roof members shall be fabricated and erected in accordance with BS 5268: Part 3.

2. Flats and gutters shall be covered with Type WBP plywood or tongued and grooved wrot boarding laid diagonally, firred to falls of not less than 1 in 120 for lead and copper and 1 in 60 for bitumen felt.

6.22   TIMBER FLOORS

1. Floor joists shall be either built into brickwork or blockwork, or held in galvanised steel joist hangers, and shall be trimmed as described in the Contract or as directed by the Engineer. Bridging shall be spaced at every 1.8 m apart and shall be 50 mm thick to the full depth of the joists or 38 mm by 50 mm herringbone strutting.

(i) Thickness of floor boarding should be described in the Contract.

(ii) If chipboard is to be used instead of floor boarding this should be described in the Contract.

2. Boarding shall be cramped up and nailed with cut flooring nails. Trimmed openings shall have mitred borders 75 mm in width.

6.23   DOOR FRAMES

1. Door frames shall be fitted into prepared openings, drilled and plugged at 3 points per jamb and shall have 100 mm by 12 mm diameter galvanised steel dowels to posts let into flooring and bedded in non-shrink or epoxy grout.

2. The joint between external door frames and adjacent walls shall be continuously pointed with gun applied butyl or other approved non-setting mastic.

6.24 WINDOWS
1. Window frames shall be securely fixed to openings in accordance with manufacturer's instructions and shall be continuously pointed with gun applied butyl or other approved non-setting mastic.

6.25 GLAZING
1. Glazing shall comply with the relevant provisions of BS 6262.

6.26 PAINTING

(i) BS 6952: Part 1 gives guidance on exterior paint protection systems.

1. Painting of structural steelwork shall comply with the relevant provisions of BS 5493. Other painting shall comply with the relevant provisions of BS 6150.

6.27 SLATING AND TILING

(i) The types and sizes of slate and tiles, together with details of any laps, battens, fixings, beddings, underfelt and boarding should be described in the Contract.

1. Slating and tiling work shall comply with the relevant provisions of BS 5534: Part 1.

6.28 LIGHTWEIGHT CONCRETE ROOF SCREEDS
1. Lightweight concrete roof screeds shall be laid to the necessary falls and shall comply with the relevant provisions of CP 144: Part 3. Before any felt is laid, a coat of bitumen primer shall be applied and allowed to dry.

6.29 ASPHALT ROOFING

(i) A written guarantee may be available for asphalt work incorporating terms currently applied by the Mastic Asphalt Council and Employers' Federation.

1. Mastic asphalt shall be laid in accordance with the relevant provisions of CP 144: Part 4 on an underlay of sheathing felt, laid loose and with joints lapped at least 50 mm. The roof shall be set out with properly formed high points, water lines and mitred bays where required.

6.30 BITUMEN FELT ROOFING
1. Built-up bitumen felt roof coverings shall be laid in accordance with the relevant provisions of CP 144: Part 3.

6.31 SURFACE TREATMENT TO FLAT ROOFS

(i) If reflective paint is to be used as an alternative to mineral aggregates, it should be described in the Contract.

1. Mineral aggregates for flat roofs shall be applied to flat asphalt and bitumen felt roofs where so described in the Contract.

6.32 PLUMBING

(i) Where heating and hot water systems are to be installed, reference should be made to BS 5449 and BS 6880: Parts 1-3.

1. Plumbing for domestic water supply shall comply with the relevant provisions of BS 6700 and local water undertaking byelaws.

6.33 OPENINGS IN WALLS, FLOORS AND CEILINGS

1. The Contractor shall box out and/or cut openings through walls, floors and ceilings for the passage of pipes and cables and, where described in the Contract, shall provide and fix in position approved tube sleeves cut off flush with the finished surface. All openings and ducts shall be sealed on completion to prevent the passage of toxic or explosive gases.

6.34 TOLERANCES FOR BUILDING WORKS

1. Tolerances for building works, except where otherwise described in the Contract, shall not exceed the permissible deviations from levels and dimensions given in BS 5606, where applicable, for the corresponding types of work.

ASSOCIATED TOPICS

1. ELECTRICAL INSTALLATIONS

Domestic wiring and other electrical installations within buildings should comply with the 'Regulations for Electrical Installations', Sixteenth Edition published by the Institution of Electrical Engineers.

To enable the Contractor to comply with the IEE Regulations certain facts (e.g. the size of cables in the incoming supply) should be described in the Contract.

2. JOINTS IN BUILDING CONSTRUCTION

For guidance on the design of joints and jointing in building construction, see BS 6093.

SECTION 7

TESTING AND DISINFECTION

General Note

The action to be taken in the event of failure to satisfy the tests specified has only been referred to in general terms where the test so requires. See Clause 36 and 39 of the Sixth Edition.

7.1 CLEANSING OF PIPELINES

1. On completion of construction, and before any disinfection, internal surfaces of pipelines shall be cleaned thoroughly in such a way as to remove all oil, grit and other deleterious matter.

7.2 PRECAUTIONS PRIOR TO TESTING PIPELINES

(i) Testing against a closed valve should not be permitted if there is any other alternative.

1. Before testing any pipeline, the Contractor shall ensure that it is anchored adequately and that thrusts from bends, branch outlets or from the pipeline ends are transmitted to solid ground or to a suitable temporary anchorage.

(ii) See also Clauses 5.1 and 5.6.

2. Open ends shall be stopped with plugs, caps or blank flanges properly jointed.

7.3 NOTIFICATION OF TEST

1. The Contractor shall notify the Engineer at least one clear working day beforehand of his intention to test a section of pipeline.

7.4 TESTING NON-PRESSURE PIPELINES

(i) The type of test (air, water, visual or CCTV) should be described in the Contract.

1. Non-pressure pipelines laid in open cut shall be tested after they are jointed and before any concreting or backfilling is commenced, other than such as may be necessary for structural stability whilst under test.

2. The pipelines shall be tested by means of an air or water test or by a visual or closed circuit television (CCTV) examination, in lengths determined by the course of construction, in accordance with a programme approved by the Engineer.

3. A further test shall be carried out after the backfilling is complete.

7.5 WATER TEST FOR NON-PRESSURE PIPELINES

(i) This clause is consistent with the provisions of BS 8005: Part 1.

1. The test pressure for non-pressure pipelines up to and including 750 mm nominal bore shall be not less than 1.2 m head of water above the pipe soffit or ground water level, whichever is the higher at the highest point, and not greater than 6 m head at the lowest point of the section. Steeply graded pipelines shall be tested in stages in cases where the maximum head, as stated above, would be exceeded if the whole section were tested in one length.

2. The pipeline shall be filled with water and a minimum period of 2 hours shall be allowed for absorption, after which water shall be added from a measuring vessel at intervals of 5 minutes and the quantity required to maintain the original water level noted. Unless otherwise specified, the length of pipeline shall be accepted if the quantity of water added over a 30 minute period is less than 0.5 litre per lineal metre per metre of nominal bore.

7.6 AIR TEST FOR NON-PRESSURE PIPELINES

1. Non-pressure pipelines to be air tested shall have air pumped in by suitable means until a pressure of 100 mm head of water is indicated in a U-tube connected to the system. The pipeline shall be accepted if the air pressure remains above 75 mm head of water after a period of 5 minutes without further pumping, following a period for stabilisation. Failure to pass the test shall not preclude acceptance of the pipeline if a successful water test, ordered by the Engineer, can subsequently be carried out in accordance with Clause 7.5.

7.7 CCTV INSPECTION OF PIPELINES

1. Where internal inspection of pipelines by CCTV is required, the Contractor shall provide all necessary equipment, including suitable covered accommodation for viewing the monitor screen, together with personnel experienced in the operation of the equipment and interpretation of results.

2. The intensity of illumination within the pipe and the rate of draw of the camera shall be such as to allow a proper examination of the inside of the pipe. Provision shall be made for the movement of the camera to be stopped and its position recorded and for permanent photographs to be taken at any point requested by the Engineer.

7.8 INFILTRATION

1. Non-pressure pipelines (including tunnels) and manholes shall be tested for infiltration after backfilling. All inlets to the system shall be effectively closed, and any residual flow shall be deemed to be infiltration.

2. The pipeline, including manholes, shall be accepted as satisfactory if the infiltration, including infiltration into manholes, in 30 minutes does not exceed 0.5 litre per lineal metre per metre of nominal bore.

3. Notwithstanding the satisfactory completion of the above test, if there is any discernible flow of water entering the pipeline at a point which can be located either by visual or CCTV inspection, the Contractor shall take such measures as are necessary to stop such infiltration.

7.9 TESTING OF PRESSURE PIPELINES

1. Gauges used for testing pressure pipelines shall either be of the conventional circular type, not less than 200 mm diameter, calibrated in metres head water, or shall have a digital indicator capable of reading increments of 0.1 m head. Before any gauge is used, the Contractor shall arrange for it to be checked independently and a dated certificate of its accuracy shall be provided.

2. Before testing, valves shall be checked and sealed, the sections of main filled with water and the air released. After having been filled, pipelines shall be left under operating pressure for the period described in the Contract, so as to achieve conditions as stable as possible for testing.

3. The pressure in the pipeline shall then be raised steadily until the specified test pressure is reached in the lowest part of the section, and the pressure shall be maintained at this level, by pumping if necessary, for a period of one hour. The pump shall then be disconnected, and no further water shall be permitted to enter the pipeline for a further period of one hour. At the end of this period the original pressure shall be restored by pumping and the loss measured by drawing off water from the pipeline until the pressure as at the end of the test is again reached.

(iv) The test pressures should be described in the Contract.

4. The permissible loss shall not exceed 2 litres per metre nominal bore per kilometre length per metre head (calculated as the average head applied to the section) per 24 hours.

5. In addition to the tests on separate sections, the whole pipeline shall be tested on completion to the same pressure and by the same procedures as that outlined for individual sections.

6. Where a new pipeline is to connect to an operational pipeline the final connection shall be inspected visually under normal operating pressure and there shall be no visible leakage.

7.10 SWABBING OF WATER MAINS

(i) The Contract should describe who provides swabs and temporary pipework, the type of swab and the maximum number of passes to be run at the Employer's expense.

1. On completion of the hydraulic test on water mains, a foam swab shall be passed through the main for final cleansing, sufficient times to achieve clear wash water.

7.11 DISINFECTION OF WATER MAINS

(i) If the Contractor is to be required to disinfect water mains, this should be described in the Contract.

1. Disinfection and bacteriological sampling of completed sections of water mains shall be carried out by the Employer. Thereafter, the main shall be regarded as operational and the Contractor shall not turn any valves or take any other action which might interfere with the use of the main.

7.12 CLEANSING OF STRUCTURES

(i) This clause deals only with structures designed to retain an aqueous liquid. For cleansing of other structures, see Clause 33 of the Sixth Edition.

1. On completion of construction, and before any disinfection, internal surfaces of structures designed to retain an aqueous liquid shall be cleaned thoroughly in such a way as to remove all oil, grit and other deleterious matter.

7.13 TESTING OF CONCRETE STRUCTURES DESIGNED TO RETAIN AN AQUEOUS LIQUID

(i) This clause is consistent with the recommendations of Clause 9.2 of BS 8007.

(ii) The 21 day stabilisation period is consistent with a design crack width of 0.2 mm or greater. The stabilisation period may be reduced to 7 days for maximum design crack width of 0.1 mm.

(iii) Clause 9.2 of BS 8007 gives guidance on retesting procedures.

1. After cleaning, and as far as practicable before any earth or other filling is placed against the outside wall faces, concrete structures designed to retain an aqueous liquid shall be filled with water at a uniform rate of not greater than 2 m in 24 hours. A period of 21 days shall be allowed by the Contractor for stabilisation, after which the water level shall be recorded by approved means at 24 hour intervals for a test period of 7 days. During the test period the total permissible drop, after allowing for evaporation and rainfall, shall not exceed 1/500 of the average water depth of the full tank or 10 mm, whichever is the less.

2. Notwithstanding the satisfactory completion of the above test, any leakage visible on the outside faces of the structure shall be stopped. Any caulking or making good of cracks in the wall section shall, where practicable, be carried out from the inside face.

7.14 TESTING OF ROOFS

(i) The Contract should describe which of the two alternative tests is required.

1. Roofs of service reservoirs shall be watertight and shall, where practicable, be tested on completion by lagooning with water to a minimum depth of 25 mm for a period of 24 hours.

2. Where it is impracticable, because of roof falls or otherwise, to contain 25 mm depth of water, the roof shall be thoroughly wetted by continuous hosing for a period of not less than 6 hours.

(ii) This clause is consistent with the recommendations of Clause 9.3 of BS 8007, which gives guidance on retesting procedures.

3. In either case, the roof shall be regarded as satisfactory if no leaks or damp patches show in the soffit.

4. The roof covering shall be completed as soon as possible after satisfactory testing.

7.15 DISINFECTION OF STRUCTURES FOR POTABLE WATER

(i) This clause will not apply if the Employer wishes to undertake disinfection.

(ii) For provisions relating to pollution of watercourses, see Clause 1.14.

1. Immediately before acceptance of any structure for potable water, the interior shall be disinfected using water chlorinated to give a residual of not less than 20 mg/l of free chlorine. The structure shall be emptied, flushed with mains water and then filled with water having a chlorine residual or not more than 0.5 mg/l free chlorine to normal top water level.

2. After 24 hours the Engineer shall arrange for a sample to be taken for bacteriological analysis. The structure shall be deemed to be disinfected if there are no coliforms in the sample. If there are coliforms in the sample the Engineer shall arrange for one further sample to be taken and the structure shall be deemed to be disinfected if there are no coliforms in that sample.

7.16 GROUT QUALITY CONTROL TESTING

(i) Grout strength requirements should be described in the Contract.

1. Where tests are required for different properties of grout, they shall be carried out on samples from the same batch.

2. The density and workability of every batch shall be determined. The density shall not differ from the value described in the Contract by more than 5%. The workability shall not differ by more than 125 mm for the 'Colcrete flow trough test' or 5 seconds for the 'Marsh cone test' with 10 mm orifice from the values described in the Contract.

3. Sampling shall be at the rate of 3 cubes taken from every 5 m^3 of grout or 50 m of grouted annulus, whichever is the smaller. When tested in accordance with the relevant provisions of BS 4551, cubes shall have a compressive strength as given in the following table:

Grout function	Minimum compressive strength at 28 days (N/mm^2)
Annulus filling:	
Type I lining	12
Type II lining	3
Exterior void filling	2

4. Cube moulds shall be 70 mm (nominal) or 100 mm and all joints shall be sealed to prevent leakage.

5. Moulds shall be overfilled and air bubbles removed by lightly tapping the mould. After leaving for 30 - 60 minutes the excess grout shall be struck off and the moulds covered with plastic sheeting or damp hessian. Moulds shall be stored at 20°C ±5°C for 24 hours, or until the grout has attained sufficient strength to allow the cube to be stripped from the mould, whichever is the greater.

6. The cubes shall be removed from the moulds, marked and stored in water at a temperature of 20°C ±1°C until tested.

ASSOCIATED TOPICS

1. TESTING OF OPERATIONAL EQUIPMENT

Testing of operational equipment installed by the Contractor should be described in item descriptions (CESMM Class A.2.6) .

2. PROVISION OF WATER FOR TESTING

The Contract should describe who is responsible for providing water for each testing operation, the points of supply, quality and programmed rates of delivery and for disposing of test water on completion, having regard to the pollution of watercourses. See Clause 1.14.

SECTION 8

ROADWORKS

General Note

This Section is not intended to cover the construction of prospectively adoptable highways but, together with the relevant materials clauses, is based generally on the requirements of the Department of Transport's 'Specification for Highway Works'; abbreviated and simplified to take account of the type of road normally required in association with water industry work.

(i) A cross-section of the carriageway construction, and the position and type of any joints, should be described in the Contract.

8.1 ROAD FORMATIONS

1. The road formation shall be the surface obtained after completion of any earthworks.

2. Formations, immediately before being covered with sub-base or road base material, shall be clean, free from mud and slurry and properly shaped and compacted to an even and uniform surface.

3. The preparation and surface treatment of formations shall be carried out after the reinstatement of any excavations for services.

8.2 SUB-BASE CONSTRUCTION

(i) If a lean-mix concrete sub-base is required, this should be described in the Contract.

1. Within 48 hours of completion of a road formation, granular sub-base material shall be spread and compacted to the required thickness. The sub-base shall be protected from deterioration due to ingress of water, the adverse effects of weather and the use of Contractors' Equipment. Compaction shall be carried out in accordance with the following table:

Type of compaction plant	Category	Number of passes for layers not greater than:		
		110 mm	150 mm	225 mm
Smooth-wheeled roller	Mass per metre width of roll:			
	over 2700 kg up to 5400 kg	16	unsuitable	unsuitable
	over 5400 kg	8	16	unsuitable
Pneumatic-tyred roller	Mass per wheel:			
	over 4000 kg up to 6000 kg	12	unsuitable	unsuitable
	over 6000 kg up to 8000 kg	12	unsuitable	unsuitable
	over 8000 kg up to 12000 kg	10	16	unsuitable
	over 12000 kg	8	12	unsuitable
Vibrating roller	Mass per metre width of vibrating roll:			
	over 700 kg up to 1300 kg	16	unsuitable	unsuitable
	over 1300 kg up to 1800 kg	6	16	unsuitable
	over 1800 kg up to 2300 kg	4	6	10
	over 2300 kg up to 2900 kg	3	5	9
	over 2900 kg up to 3600 kg	3	5	8
	over 3600 kg up to 4300 kg	2	4	7
	over 4300 kg up to 5000 kg	2	4	6
	over 5000 kg	2	3	5
Vibrating-plate compactor	Mass per unit area of base plate:			
	over 1400 kg/m^2 up to 1800 kg/m^2	8	unsuitable	unsuitable
	over 1800 kg/m^2 up to 2100 kg/m^2	5	8	unsuitable
	over 2100 kg/m^2	3	6	10
Vibro-tamper	Mass:			
	over 50 kg up to 65 kg	4	8	unsuitable
	over 65 kg up to 75 kg	3	6	10
	over 75 kg	2	4	8
Power rammer	Mass:			
	100 kg - 500 kg	5	8	unsuitable
	over 500 kg	5	8	12

8.3   WET-MIX MACADAM CONSTRUCTION

1. Wet-mix macadam shall be spread evenly on the sub-base and compacted in layers of not more than 200 mm thickness at the optimum moisture content ±0.5%.

2. Spreading shall be undertaken concurrently with placing. Compaction shall be completed as soon as possible after the material has been spread and carried out in accordance with the table in Clause 8.2.

8.4   LEAN CONCRETE CONSTRUCTION

1. Lean concrete construction for roads shall be Grade C7.5 and shall be spread evenly on the sub-base and laid and compacted in layers of not more than 200 mm thickness.

2. Spreading shall be undertaken concurrently with placing. Compaction shall be completed as soon as possible after the material has been spread and carried out in accordance with the table in Clause 8.2. The maximum period of time between mixing of the materials and final compacting of any given material shall be 2 hours.

3. Where practicable, joints against hardened material shall be avoided. Where such joints are unavoidable, the hardened material shall be cut back vertically for the full depth of the layer before placing any further adjacent material.

4. Lean concrete shall be cured for a period of not less than 7 days. No vehicular traffic shall be allowed to run on the base during this time.

8.5   LAYING COATED MACADAM

(i) BS 4987: Part 2 covers the laying of macadam carriageways, footways and other lightly trafficked areas.

1. Transportation, laying and compaction of all coated macadam shall be carried out in accordance with the relevant provisions of BS 4987: Part 2.

8.6   LAYING HOT ROLLED ASPHALT

1. Transportation, laying and compaction of hot rolled asphalt shall be carried out in accordance with the relevant provisions of BS 594: Part 2.

8.7   WATERPROOF UNDERLAY FOR CONCRETE CARRIAGEWAYS

1. Waterproof underlay shall consist of waterproof paper or impermeable plastic sheeting, laid to provide a membrane immediately below the concrete. Overlaps shall be not less than 300 mm and precautions shall be taken to prevent ponding on the membrane.

8.8   REINFORCEMENT OF CONCRETE CARRIAGEWAYS

(i) This clause assumes that only a single layer of reinforcement is necessary.

1. Reinforcement in concrete carriageways shall be so placed that, after compaction of the concrete, its cover below the finished surface of the slab is 60 mm (±10 mm) and it terminates 125 mm (±25 mm) from the edges of the slab and all pre-formed joints in the concrete.

2. At transverse joints between mats of steel fabric reinforcement, the longitudinal bars shall overlap by at least 35 times the bar diameter, provided that such overlap shall not in any case be less than 450 mm. Mats shall be placed so as to maintain the same spacing between edge longitudinal bars as in the body of the mat.

3. Reinforcement shall be positioned above dowel bars and tie bars irrespective of the tolerances on position.

8.9 LAYING CONCRETE CARRIAGEWAYS

(i) The positioning and detailing of movement joints should be described in the Contract.

1. Placing, compacting and finishing of concrete in carriageways shall be carried out in one layer as rapidly as possible and shall be so arranged that, in any transverse section, the time for completion of mixing the first batch of concrete to completion of compaction of that section shall not exceed 2 hours.

2. Carriageway surfaces shall have a Screeded Finish, which shall be brushed transversely to produce a lightly brushmarked finish, with a 100 mm arris Steel Trowel Finish to sides and at joints.

3. Surface irregularities shall not exceed 3 mm when checked with a 3 m straight edge.

8.10 LAYING KERBS AND CHANNELS

(i) Details of the concrete bed and haunch should be described in the Contract.

1. Kerbs, edgings, channels and quadrants shall be laid and bedded on a layer of Class M1 mortar, either on the concrete carriageway or on a Grade C20 concrete foundation, as described in the Contract. They shall be butt-jointed except where otherwise described in the Contract, save that where laid on concrete carriageways they shall be provided with joints coincident with the carriageway movement joints, of width and with filler identical to that used in the carriageway joints. All kerbs shall be backed with Grade C20 concrete.

2. For radii of 12 m or less, kerbs and channels of the appropriate radius shall be used.

3. Alignment of kerbs and channels shall not deviate from that described in the Contract by more than 10 mm, with no lipping of visible faces.

8.11 FOUNDATIONS FOR FOOTWAYS

(i) A cross-section of the footway construction should be described in the Contract.

1. Foundations for footways shall consist of Type 1 granular sub-base material spread evenly and compacted in layers of not more than 100 mm thickness.

2. Compaction to the correct levels shall be carried out using a vibratory roller having a static load of at least 1000 kg/m width of roll.

8.12 LAYING CONCRETE PAVING FLAGS

1. Precast concrete flags shall be laid to the required falls on sub-base material as described in the Contract, bonded with joints at right angles to the kerb, and spot bedded with Class M4 mortar with no lipping of top surfaces.

2. Flags shall be cut to fit around surface boxes and other furniture and, on circular work where the radius is 12m or less, shall be radially cut on both edges to the required lines.

8.13 TOLERANCES FOR FINISHED CARRIAGEWAY SURFACES

1. Finished surfaces at each stage of road construction shall not vary from the levels described in the Contract by more than the following permissible deviations:

Surface	Permissible deviation (mm)
Formation and sub-base	+10, -30
Base	±15
Wearing surface or slab surface	±6

2. The combination of permitted tolerances in the levels of different pavement courses shall not result in a reduction in thickness of the pavement, excluding the sub-base, by more than 15 mm from the specified thickness, nor a reduction in the thickness of the bituminous wearing course by more than 5 mm from that specified, and the maximum allowable irregularity of the wearing surface below a 3 m straight edge shall be 3 mm.

8.14 FIXING OF GULLIES

1. Gullies shall be bedded and surrounded with Grade C20 concrete to the thickness described in the Contract.

2. Frames shall be bedded in Class M1 mortar on two courses of Class 'B' engineering brickwork or precast concrete gully cover slabs.

SECTION 9

SEWER AND WATER MAIN RENOVATION

General Note

This Section covers the fundamental requirements of sewer and water main renovation based on the recommendations of the 'Sewerage Rehabilitation Manual' and the 'Water Mains Rehabilitation Manual'.

Special Specification Clauses will normally be required to describe the particular renovation system required, whether or not a proprietary system is to be used.

Whenever a proprietary renovation system is offered, a described methods statement should be called for and its suitability assessed before acceptance of the tender. Guidance on the assessment of renovation systems is given in the Sewerage and Water Mains Rehabilitation Manuals.

The Contract should describe any special requirements such as where the liquid transported is unusually aggressive or where additional protection is required.

(i) See 1.AT.14 of Section 1.

(ii) Example flow schedules are given in the 'Sewerage Rehabilitation Manual'.

(iii) Where the Contractor will be permitted to operate valves and isolate flows, this should be described in the Contract.

9.1 ISOLATION OF FLOWS
1. Flows shall be positively dealt with or isolated from the section under renovation.

(i) Any requirement for a structural condition survey shall be described in the Contract.

9.2 PREPARATORY SURVEY
1. The Contractor shall carry out a survey of the sewers to be renovated to determine the position, size and angle of approach of all laterals, to an accuracy appropriate to the method of reconnection.

2. The Contractor shall carry out a survey of the water mains to be renovated to determine their position and size and the position and condition of fittings.

3. Where described in the Contract a survey of the current structural condition of the sewers or water mains shall also be carried out.

(i) Where the Contractor will be permitted to operate valves and hydrants, this should be described in the Contract.

4. Valves and hydrants shall be checked to ensure that all are accessible and operable.

9.3 PREPARATION OF EXISTING SEWERS AND WATER MAINS
1. Sewers and water mains to be renovated shall be prepared so that the installation and performance of the renovation system is not impaired.

2. The Contractor shall take all precautions necessary to prevent debris being carried downstream whilst preparing or working in existing sewers and water mains.

9.4 JOINTING GENERALLY

1. Jointing surfaces and components shall be kept clean and free from extraneous matter until the joints have been made or assembled.

9.5 CONNECTIONS

1. All laterals, branches and service connections shall be reconnected and any circumferential lining joints shall not be made at or within 100 mm of a connection.

2. Each finished connection shall be made flush with the lining and shall provide a smooth transition.

3. No connection shall be made to a sliplining system until the latter has relaxed sufficiently to prevent damage.

9.6 INTERMEDIATE CHAMBERS

1. The Contractor shall ensure that at intermediate chambers the edges of the lining are adequately sealed where applicable and the benching made good.

9.7 RELEASE OF CURING WATER

1. Whenever hot water curing of a lining system is carried out the water shall not be released until it cools below 40°C.

9.8 ANNULUS GROUTING GENERALLY

1. All air, water and contaminated grout is to be expelled from the annulus by the grouting process.

(i) Any alternative restrictions on maximum grout pressures should be described in the Contract.

2. The grout injection pressure shall be continuously measured by a suitable gauge fitted at the injection nozzle and shall not exceed 50 kN/m^2 unless otherwise described in the Contract.

3. The quantity of grout injected at each injection point and the maximum pressure at the nozzle at that point shall be recorded.

9.9 INSPECTION AFTER GROUTING

1. Immediately after each grouting operation the Contractor shall inspect the sewer main, branches or laterals and clean out any excess grout.

9.10 LINING THROUGH VALVES

1. Any valves lined in-situ shall be operated throughout their full travel several times immediately after lining in order to ensure free operation. There shall be no in-situ lining through valves of pipelines of non-man entry sizes.

9.11 INSPECTION AFTER RENOVATION

(i) The format of the information required and any need for a CCTV survey should be described in the Contract.

1. On completion of the renovation the Contractor shall undertake a survey and provide a record of that survey to the Engineer.

2. The Contractor shall take and provide the Engineer with pipe samples in order to check lining performance and to determine thickness. The Contractor shall make good after the samples have been taken. The monitoring of renovation will be used to determine the location of samples.

(ii) The number of samples to be removed, and the length of the sample should be described in the Contract. Where appropriate a control sample shall be provided by the Contractor, in advance of the renovation commencing, to compare with samples taken at completion.

9.12   BRINGING RENOVATED WATER MAINS INTO SERVICE

1. Before returning any renovated water main into service, the Contractor shall clean and disinfect it in accordance with Clauses 7.1, 7.10 and 7.11.

APPENDIX I

INCORPORATION OF SPECIFICATION INTO CONTRACTS

It is not necessary to bind copies of the Civil Engineering Specification for the Water Industry, 4th Edition, into the documents prepared for tenderers or into any formally sealed contract.

Supplementary Clauses should be included in the Contract documents and numbered in two separate groups as follows:

(a)   Specification requirements which are related to an existing clause should be numbered as additional sub-clauses (e.g. requirements for special flanges other than to BS 4504 should be numbered 2.47.2).

(b)   New clauses unrelated to existing clauses should be numbered to follow the last clause of the appropriate Section.

The Specification should be incorporated by reference by including the following provisions, in tender documents, immediately preceding the Supplementary Specification Clauses:

SPECIFICATION

1.   The Specification referred to in the Tender shall be the 'Civil Engineering Specification for the Water Industry, 4th Edition', published by the Water Services Association in October 1993, augmented by the Supplementary Clauses.

2.   In so far as any Supplementary Clause may conflict or be inconsistent with any provision of the Civil Engineering Specification for the Water Industry, 4th Edition, the Supplementary Clause shall always prevail.

APPENDIX II

List of British Standard Specifications to which reference is made in the document.

BS	TITLE	REFERENCE(S)
4	Structural steel sections	
	Part 1: Hot-rolled sections	2.68.1
*12	Portland cement	2.15.1, 2.15.3, 2.15(vii) 4.15.1
*65	Vitrified clay pipes, fittings and ducts,	2.27.1, 2.27.2, 2.43.1,
	also flexible mechanical joints for use solely with	2.44.2, 2.59.2
	surface water pipes and fittings	
*146	Portland blastfurnace cement	2.15.1, 2.15(iv)
187	Calcium silicate (sandlime and flintlime) bricks	2.105.1
*EN 295	Vitrified clay pipes and fittings and pipe joints for	2.27.1, 2.59.2
	drains and sewers	
EN 301	Adhesives, phenolic and aminoplastic, for load-bearing	2.82.1
	timber structures: classification and performance	
	requirements	
EN 302	Adhesives for load-bearing timber structures: test methods	2.82.1
402	Clay roofing tiles and fittings	
	*Part 1: Plain tiles and fittings	2.102.1
*410	Test sieves	2.117.1, 2.118.1
416	Discharge and ventilating pipes and fittings, sand-cast	
	or spun in cast iron	
	*Part 1: Spigot and socket systems	2.39.1
	*Part 2: Socketless systems	2.39.1
417	Galvanized low carbon steel cisterns, cistern lids,	
	tanks and cylinders	
	Part 2: Metric units	2.40.1
434	Bitumen road emulsions (anionic and cationic)	
	Part 1: Bitumen road emulsions	2.121.1
435	Dressed natural stone kerbs, channels, quadrants and	2.111.1
	setts	
459	Matchboarded wooden door leaves for external use	2.88.1
460	Cast iron rainwater goods	2.38.1
*473 & 550	Concrete roofing tiles and fittings	2.102.1
486	Asbestos-cement pressure pipes and joints	2.33.2
493	Airbricks and gratings for wall ventilation	2.105.4, 2.105(iii)
497	Manhole covers, road gully gratings and frames for	
	drainage purposes	
	* Part 1: Cast iron and cast steel	2.57.1, 2.60.1
534	Steel pipes, joints and specials for water and sewage	2.29.1, 5.11(i)
544	Linseed oil putty for use in wooden frames	2.93.1
569	Asbestos-cement rainwater goods	2.38.1
594	Hot rolled asphalt for roads and other paved areas	
	Part 1: Constituent materials and asphalt mixtures	2.120.1
	Part 2: Transport, laying and compaction of rolled	
	asphalt	8.6.1
639	Covered carbon and carbon manganese steel	
	electrodes for manual metal-arch welding	2.71.2
644	Wood windows	
	*Part 1: Factors assembled windows of various types	2.90.1
	Part 2: Wood double hung sash windows	2.90.1
	Part 3: Wood double hung sash and case windows	2.90.1
	(Scottish type)	

BS	TITLE	REFERENCE(S)
680	Roofing slates	
	*Part 2: Metric Units	2.102.1
690	Asbestos-cement slates and sheets	
	Part 2: Asbestos-cement and cellulose-asbestos-cement flat sheets	2.102.1
	Part 4: Slates	2.102.1
	Part 5: Lining sheets and panels	2.102.1
729	Hot dip galvanized coatings on iron and steel articles	2.73.1, 2.74.2, 2.75.2, 2.76.2 2.77.1, 2.77.2, 2.108.3, 2.109.3
743	Materials for damp-proof courses	2.52.2, 2.127(i)
747	Roofing felts	2.102.1
750	Underground fire hydrants and surface box frames and covers	2.61.1
812	Testing aggregates	
	Part 2: Methods for determination of physical properties	2.10.3
	Part 103: Method for determination of particle size distribution	2.117.4, 2.118.2
	Part 105: Methods for determination of particle shape	2.118.3
	Part 111: Methods for determination of ten percent fines value (TFV)	2.117.5
	Part 124: Method for determination of frost-heave	2.117.2
864	Capillary and compression tube fittings of copper and copper alloy	
	*Part 2: Capillary and compression fittings for copper tubes	2.40.1
	Part 5: Compression fittings for polyethylene pipes with outside diameters to BS 5556	2.40.1
882	Aggregates from natural sources for concrete	2.10.1, 2.10.2, 2.11.1 2.12.2, 2.12.4, 4.7.1
*890	Building limes	2.17.1
903	Physical testing of rubber	
	Part A1: Determination of density	2.126.2
	Part A2: Determination of tensile stress-strain properties	2.126.2
	Part A16: Determination of the effect of liquids	2.126.2
	Part A26: Determination of hardness	2.126.2
952	Glass for glazing	
	Part 1: Classification	2.92.1
	Part 2: Terminology for work on glass	2.92(i)
970	Wrought steels for mechanical and allied engineering purposes	
	Part 1: General inspection and testing procedures and specific requirements for carbon, carbon manganese alloy and stainless steels	2.72.4, 2.73.2, 2.74.1 2.75.3, 2.77.1, 2.77.2
1010	Draw-off taps and stop valves for water services (screw-down pattern)	2.15.3
	*Part 2: Draw-off taps and above-ground stopvalves	2.40.1
1014	Pigments for Portland cement and Portland cement products	2.15.3
1047	Air-cooled blastfurnace slag aggregate for use in construction	2.10.1, 2.10.2
1052	Mild steel wire for general engineering purposes	2.22.1
1070	Black paint (tar-based)	2.69.3
*1125	WC flushing cisterns (including dual flush cisterns and flush pipes)	2.40.1
*1142	Fibre building boards	2.52.1, 2.52(i), 2.98.1
1161	Aluminium alloy sections for structural purposes	2.70.1

BS	TITLE	REFERENCE(S)
1178	Milled lead sheet for building purposes	2.67.1, 2.104.1
1186	Timber for and workmanship in joinery	
	Part 1: Timber	2.85.1
	Part 2: Workmanship	6.19.2
	Part 3: Wood trim and its fixing	2.86.1, 2.86(i)
1188	Ceramic wash basins and pedestals	2.40.1
1191	Gypsum building plasters	
	Part 2: Premixed lightweight plasters	2.95.1, 2.95.2
1196	Clayware field drain pipes and junctions	2.43.1
1199 and 1200	Building sands from natural sources	2.12.1, 2.12.3, 2.12.4
1202	Nails	
	Part 1: Steel nails	2.79.1
	Part 2: Copper nails	2.79.1
	Part 3: Aluminium nails	2.79.1
1206	Fireclay sinks: dimensions and workmanship	2.40.1
1212	Float operated valves	
	Part 2: Diaphragm type float operated valves (copper alloy body, excluding floats)	2.40.1
	*Part 3: Diaphragm type float operated valves (plastics bodied) for cold water services only (excluding floats)	2.40.1
*1217	Cast stone	2.112.1
1230	Gypsum plasterboard	
	Part 1: Plasterboard excluding materials submitted to secondary operations	2.98.1
1243	Metal ties for cavity wall construction	2.106.1
1244	Metal sinks for domestic purposes	
	*Part 2: Sit-on and inset sinks	2.40.1
1247	Manhole steps	
	*Part 1: Galvanized ferrous or stainless steel manhole steps	2.58.1
	Part 2: Plastics encapsulated manhole steps	2.58.1
	Part 3: Aluminium manhole steps	2.58.1
*1254	WC seats (plastics)	2.40.1
1285	Wood surrounds for steel windows and doors	2.90.1
1297	Tongued and grooved softwood flooring	2.87.1
1329	Metal hand rinse basins	2.40.1
1336	Knotting	2.94.3
1369	Steel lathing for internal plastering and external rendering	
	Part 1: Expanded metal and ribbed lathing	2.96.1
1370	Low heat Portland cement	2.15.1
1377	Methods of test for soils for civil engineering purposes	
	Part 2: Classification tests	2.117.4
	Part 4: Compaction-related tests	2.14.3
1387	Screwed and socketed steel tubes and tubulars and plain end steel tubes suitable for welding or for screwing to BS 21 pipe threads	2.74.1
1438	Media for biological percolating filters	2.18.1, 2.18(ii), 2.18(iii)
1449	Steel plate, sheet and strip	
	Part 2: Stainless and heat-resisting steel plate, sheet and strip	2.72.4, 2.75.3, 2.77.1, 2.77.2
1470	Wrought aluminium and aluminium alloys for general engineering purposes: plate, sheet and strip	2.70.1

BS	TITLE	REFERENCE(S)
1471	Wrought aluminium and aluminium alloys for general engineering purposes - drawn tube	2.70.1, 2.74.1
1474	Wrought aluminium and aluminium alloys for general engineering purposes: bars, extruded round tubes and sections	2.70.1, 2.74.1, 2.75.4
1490	Aluminium and aluminium alloy ingots and castings for general engineering purposes	2.70.1, 2.74.1
1494	Fixing accessories for building purposes	
	Part 1: Fixings for sheet, roof and wall coverings	2.78.1
1521	Waterproof building papers	2.25.1
1567	Wood door frames and linings	2.88.1, 2.88(ii)
1579	Connectors for timber	2.80.1
1615	Method for specifying anodic oxidation coatings on aluminium and its alloys	2.74.2, 2.75.5
1706	Method for specifying electroplated coatings of zinc and cadmium on iron and steel	2.77.2
1710	Identification of pipelines and services	2.44(ii)
1722	Fences	
	Part 1: Chain link fences	2.107.1, 2.107.2, 2.107(i)
	Part 2: Rectangular wire mesh and hexagonal wire netting fences	2.107.1, 2.107.2, 2.107(i)
	Part 3: Strained wire fences	2.107.1, 2.107.2, 2.107(i)
	Part 4: Cleft chestnut pale fences	2.107.1, 2.107.2, 2.107(i)
	Part 5: Close boarded fences	2.107.1, 2.107.2, 2.107(i)
	Part 6: Wooden palisade fences	2.107.1, 2.107.2, 2.107(i)
	Part 7: Wooden post and rail fences	2.107.1, 2.107.2, 2.107(i)
	Part 8: Mild steel (low carbon steel) continuous bar fences	2.107.1, 2.107.2, 2.107(i)
	Part 9: Mild steel (low carbon steel) fences with round or square verticals and flat horizontals	2.107.1, 2.107.2, 2.107(i)
	Part 10: Anti-intruder fences in chain link and welded mesh	2.107.1, 2.107.2, 2.107(i)
	Part 11: Woven wood and lap boarded panel fences	2.107.1, 2.107.2, 2.107(i)
	Part 12: Steel palisade fences	2.107.1, 2.107.2, 2.107(i)
	Part 13: Chain link fences for tennis courts surrounds	2.107.1, 2.107.2, 2.107(i)
	Part 14: Open mesh steel panel fences	2.107.1, 2.107.2, 2.107(i)
1876	Automatic flushing cisterns for urinals	2.40.1
1968	Floats for ballvalves (copper)	2.40.1
*2456	Floats (plastics) for float operated valves for cold water services	2.40.1
*2494	Elastomeric seals for joints in pipework and pipelines	2.46.1, 2.48.1
2499	Hot-applied joint sealants for concrete pavements	2.125.2, 2.125(i)
2523	Lead-based priming paints	2.94.6
2592	Thermoplastic flooring tiles	2.100.1
2789	Spheroidal graphite or nodular graphite cast iron	2.72.2
2871	Copper and copper alloys. Tubes	
	*Part 1: Copper tubes for water, gas and sanitation	2.40.1
*2879	Draining taps (screw-down pattern)	2.40.1
2901	Filler rods and wires for gas-shielding arc welding	
	Part 1: Ferritic steels	2.71.4
	Part 2: Stainless steels	2.71.4
	Part 4: Aluminium and aluminium alloys and magnesium alloys	2.71.4
2926	Chromium and chromium-nickel steel electrodes for manual metal-arc welding	2.71.2

BS	TITLE	REFERENCE(S)
2971	Class II arc welding of carbon steel pipework for carrying fluids	5.11(i)
2994	Cold rolled steel sections	2.68.1
2997	Aluminium rainwater goods	2.38.1
3148	Methods of test for water for making concrete (including notes on the suitability of the water)	2.9(ii)
3251	Indicator plates for fire hydrants and emergency water supplies	2.61.3
3260	Semi-flexible PVC floor tiles	2.100.1
3261	Unbacked flexible PVC flooring	
	Part 1: Homogeneous flooring	2.100.1
3380	Wastes (excluding skeleton sink wastes) and bath overflows	2.39.2
3382	Electroplated coatings on threaded components	
	Part 1: Cadmium on steel components	2.77.2
	Part 2: Zinc on steel components	2.77.2
3416	Bitumen-based coatings for cold application, suitable for use in contact with potable water	2.69.3
3470	Field gates and posts	2.108.1, 2.108.2
*3505	Unplasticized polyvinyl chloride (PVC-U) pressure pipes for cold potable water	2.32.1, 2.32(iii), 2.40.1, 2.44.1
*3506	Unplasticized PVC pipe for industrial uses	2.44.1
3601	Carbon steel pipes and tubes with specified room temperature properties for pressure purposes	2.29.1, 5.11(i)
3656	Asbestos-cement pipes, joints and fittings for sewerage and drainage	2.33.1, 2.44.2
3698	Calcium plumbate priming paints	2.94.6
3761	Solvent-based paint remover	2.94.7
3797	Lightweight aggregates for masonry units and structural concrete	2.10.1, 2.10.2
3837	Expanded polystyrene boards	
	Part 1: Boards manufactured from expandable beads	2.98.1
3882	Recommendations and classification for top soil	2.4.1
3892	Pulverized-fuel ash	
	*Part 1: Pulverized-fuel ash for use as a cementitious component in structural concrete	2.14.2, 2.15.1
	*Part 2: Pulverized-fuel ash for use in grouts and for miscellaneous uses in concrete	2.14.1
*3921	Clay bricks	2.105.1
3936	Nursery stock	
	Part 1: Trees and shrubs	2.8.1
*3943	Plastics waste traps	2.39.3
3969	Recommendations for turf for general purposes	2.5.1, 2.5(ii)
3998	Recommendations for tree work	3.11.3
4022	Prefabricated gypsum wallboard panels	2.98.1
*4027	Sulfate-resisting Portland cement	2.15.1, 4.15.1
4043	Recommendations for transplanting root-balled trees	2.8.1, 3.11.1, 3.11.2
4131	Terrazzo tiles	2.100.1
4165	Electrode wires and fluxes for the submerged arc welding of carbon steel and medium-tensile steel	2.71.3
4190	ISO metric black hexagon bolts, screws and nuts	2.72.1
4211	Ladders for permanent access to chimneys, other high structures, silos and bins	2.75.1, 2.75.3, 2.75.4

BS	TITLE	REFERENCE(S)
*4213	Cold water storage and combined feed and expansion cisterns (polyolefin or olefin copolymer) up to 500L capacity used for domestic purposes	2.40.1
*4246	High slag blastfurnace cement	2.15.1
4248	Supersulphated cement	2.15.1
*4254	Two-part polysulphide-based sealants	2.125.4
4320	Metal washers for general engineering purposes. Metric series	2.72.1
4346	Joints and fittings for use with unplasticized PVC pressure pipes	
	*Part 1: Injection moulded unplasticized PVC fittings for solvent welding for use with pressure pipes, including potable water supply	2.32.1, 2.40.1
	*Part 2: Mechanical joints and fittings, principally of unplasticized PVC	2.32.1, 2.40.1
	*Part 3: Solvent cement	2.32.1, 2.32.4
4360	Weldable structural steels 2.74.1, 6.20.1	2.44.1, 2.68.1, 2.69.1
4363	Distribution assemblies for electricity supplies for construction and building sites	1.20(ii)
4375	Unsintered PTFE tape for thread sealing applications	2.41.1
4395	High strength friction grip bolts and associated nuts and washers for structural engineering	
	Part 1: General grade	2.72.1
	Part 2: Higher grade bolts and nuts and general grade washers	2.72.1
	Part 3: Higher grade bolts (waisted shank) nuts and general grade washers	2.72.1
4449	Carbon steel bars for the reinforcement of concrete	2.21.1, 2.122.1
4466	Scheduling, dimensioning, bending and cutting of steel reinforcement for concrete	4.21.1, 4.21.2
4471	Sizes of sawn and processed softwood	2.85.2
4482	Cold reduced steel wire for the reinforcement of concrete	2.21.1
4483	Steel fabric for the reinforcement of concrete	2.21.1
4504	Circular flanges for pipes, valves and fittings (PN designated)	
	Section 3.1: Steel flanges	2.47.1, 2.47(ii), 2.72.2
	Section 3.2: Cast iron flanges	2.47.1, 2.47(ii), 2.72.2
*4514	Unplasticized PVC soil and ventilating pipes, fittings and accessories	2.39.1
4515	Welding of steel pipelines on land and offshore	5.11.1, 5.11(i)
4551	Methods of testing mortars, screeds and plasters	7.16.3
4576	Unplasticized polyvinyl chloride (PVC-U) rainwater goods and accessories	
	*Part 1: Half-round gutters and pipes of circular cross-section	2.38.1
4592	Industrial type metal flooring, walkways and stair treads	
	*Part 1: Open bar gratings	2.76.1, 2.76(i)
	*Part 2: Expanded metal grating panels	2.76.1, 2.76(i)
	*Part 3: Cold formed planks	2.76.1, 2.76(i)
*4625	Prestressed concrete pressure pipes (including fittings)	2.30.1, 2.30(i)
4652	Metallic zinc-rich priming paint (organic media)	2.94.6
*4660	Unplasticized polyvinyl chloride (PVC-U) pipes and plastics fittings of nominal sizes 110 and 160 for below ground gravity drainage and sewerage	2.32.2, 2.32.4, 2.44.2
4721	Ready-mix building mortars	2.20.2, 2.20(i)

BS	TITLE	REFERENCE(S)
4729	Dimensions of bricks of special shapes and sizes	2.105.3
4756	Ready mixed aluminium priming paints for woodwork	2.94.5
*4772	Ductile iron pipes and fittings	2.31.1, 2.31(ii), 2.47(i)
4787	Internal and external wood doorsets, door leaves and frames	
	Part 1: Dimensional requirements	2.88.1
4800	Paint colours for building purposes	2.94.1
4841	Rigid urethane foam for building applications	
	Part 1: Laminated board for general purposes	2.98.1
	Part 2: Laminated board for use as a wall and ceiling insulation	2.98.1
4848	Hot-rolled structural steel sections	
	Part 2: Hot-finished hollow sections	2.44.1, 2.68.1
	Part 4: Equal and unequal angles	2.68.1
4865	Dimensions of gaskets for pipe flanges to BS 4504	
	Part 1: Non-metallic flat gaskets (including gaskets for flanges to BS 4722)	2.48.1
*4873	Aluminium alloy windows	2.90.1
4880	Urinals	
	Part 1: Stainless steel slab urinals	2.40.1
4887	Mortar admixtures	
	*Part 1: Air-entraining (plasticizing) admixtures	2.20.3
	Part 2: Set retarding admixtures	2.20.3
4928	Man-made fibre ropes	2.45.1
4942	Short link chain for lifting purposes	
	Part 2: Grade M(4) non-calibrated chain	2.73.1, 2.73.2
*4962	Plastics pipes and fittings for use as sub soil field drains	2.43.1
4965	Decorative laminated plastics sheet veneered boards and panels	2.98.1
*4978	Softwood grades for structural use	2.84.1, 2.84(ii)
4987	Coated macadam for roads and other paved areas	
	Part 1: Constituent materials and mixtures	2.119.1
	Part 2: Transport, laying and compaction	8.5.1, 8.3(i)
4991	Propylene copolymer pressure pipe	2.37.1
5075	Concrete admixtures	
	Part 1: Accelerating admixtures, retarding admixtures and water reducing admixtures	2.16.1
	Part 2: Air-entraining admixtures	2.16.1
	Part 3: Super plasticizing admixtures	2.16.1
5080	Structural fixings in concrete and masonry	
	Part 1: Method of test for tensile loading	2.77.3, 2.77(iv)
	Part 2: Method for determination of resistance to loading in shear	2.77.3
*5082	Water-borne priming paints for woodwork	2.94.5
5114	Performance requirements for joints and compression fittings for use with polyethylene pipes	2.40.1
5135	Arc welding of carbon and carbon manganese steels	5.11(i)
*5150	Cast iron gate valves	2.49.1
5151	Cast iron gate (parallel slide) valves for general purposes	2.49.1
*5153	Cast iron check valves for general purposes	2.49.1
*5154	Copper alloy globe, globe stop and check, check and gate valves	2.49.1
*5155	Butterfly valves	2.49.1
5156	Diagphragm valves	2.49.1
5158	Cast iron plug valves	2.49.1

BS	TITLE	REFERENCE(S)
*5163	Predominantly key-operated cast iron gate valves for waterworks purposes	2.49.1
*5178	Prestressed concrete pipes for drainage and sewerage	2.30.1, 2.30(i)
5212	Cold applied joint sealant systems for concrete pavements	
	*Part 1: Joint sealants	2.125.3, 2.125(i)
5224	Masonry cement	2.15.1, 2.15(iii)
*5254	Polypropylene waste pipe and fittings (external diameter 34.6mm, 41.0 mm and 54.1 mm)	2.39.1
*5255	Thermoplastics waste pipe and fittings	2.39.1
5270	Bonding agents for use with gypsum plasters and cement	
	Part 1: Polyvinyl acetate (PVAC) emulsion bonding agents for indoor use with gypsum building plasters	2.95.2
5328	Concrete	
	*Part 1: Guide to specifying concrete	2.10(iii), 2.15(iii), 2.15(vi) 2.16(i), 4.3(v), 4.8.1
	*Part 2: Methods for specifying concrete mixes	4.1(v), 4.3.1, 4.4(ii), 4.10.1
	*Part 3: Procedures to be used in producing and transporting concrete	4.1.1, 4.2.3, 4.3.1, 4.3.2, 4.4.1, 4.4.4, 4.10.1, 4.12.1
	*Part 4: Procedures to be used in sampling, testing and assessing compliance of concrete	2.63.2, 4.1.1, 4.8(ii), 4.9.2
*5358	Solvent-borne priming paints for woodwork	2.94.5
5391	Acrylonitrile-butadiene-styrene (ABS) pressure pipe	
	*Part 1: Pipe for industrial uses	2.35.1
5392	Acrylonitrile-butadiene-styrene (ABS) fittings for use with ABS pressure pipe	
	*Part 1: Fittings for use with pipe for industrial uses	2.35.1
5412 & 5413	Performance of draw-off taps with metal bodies for water services and with plastics bodies for water services	
	Part 1: Dimensional and design characteristics	2.40.1
	Part 2: Water tightness and pressure resistance characteristics	2.40.1
	Part 3: Hydraulic characteristics	2.40.1
	Part 4: Mechanical and endurance characteristics	2.40.1
	Part 5: Physio-chemical characteristics: materials, coatings	2.40.1
5433	Underground stopvalves for water services	2.40.1
5450	Size of hardwoods and methods of measurement	2.85.2
5480	Glass reinforced plastics (GRP) pipes, joints and fittings for use for water supply or sewerage	2.34.1
*5481	Unplasticized PVC pipe and fittings for gravity sewers	2.32.2, 2.44.2
5503	Vitreous china washdown WC pans with horizontal outlet	
	Part 1: Connecting dimensions	2.40.1
	Part 2: Materials, quality, performance and dimensions other than connecting dimensions	2.40.1
5520	Vitreous china bowl urinals (rimless type)	2.40.1
5627	Plastics connectors for use with horizontal outlet vitreous china WC pans	2.40.1
5642	Sills and copings	
	Part 1: Window sills of precast concrete, cast stone, clayware, slate and natural stone	2.91.1
	Part 2: Copings of precast concrete, cast stone clayware, slate and natural stone	2.113.1

BS	TITLE	REFERENCE(S)
5669	Particleboards	
	*Part 2: Wood chipboard	2.87.2
	Part 4: Cement bonded particleboard	2.98.1
5709	Stiles bridle gates and kissing gates	2.109.1, 2.109.2
5834	Surface boxes, guards and underground chambers for gas and waterworks purposes	
	Part 1: Guards, including foundation units	2.62.2, 2.62(i)
	*Part 2: Small surface boxes	2.62.1, 2.62(i)
	*Part 3: Large surface boxes	2.62.1, 2.62(i)
5835	Recommendations for testing of aggregates	
	Part 1: Compactibility test for graded aggregates	2.118.4
5889	One-part gun grade silicone-based sealants	2.125.5
5911	Precast concrete pipes, fittings and ancillary products	
	*Part 2: Inspection chambers and street gullies	2.59.1
	Part 110: Ogee pipes and fittings (including perforated)	2.28.1, 2.28(i), 2.43.1
	*Part 100: Unreinforced and reinforced pipes and fittings with flexible joints	2.28.1, 2.28(i), 2.30.2 2.44.2, 2.63.6
	Part 114: Porous pipes	2.43.1
	*Part 120: Reinforced jacking pipes with flexible joints	2.28(i), 2.28.3, 5.25.5
	*Part 200: Unreinforced and reinforced manholes and soakaways of circular cross section	2.55.1, 2.55(i), 2.56.1
5977	Lintels	
	Part 1: Method for assessment of load	2.89(ii)
	*Part 2: Prefabricated lintels	2.89.1
6073	Precast concrete masonry units	
	*Part 1: Precast concrete masonry units	2.105.1
	*Part 2: Method for specifying precast concrete masonry units	2.105.1
6076	Tubular polyethylene film for use as a protective sleeving for buried iron pipes and fittings	2.26.1, 2.26.2
*6087	Flexible joints for grey or ductile cast iron drainpipes and fittings (BS 437) and for discharge and ventilating pipes and fittings (BS 416)	2.38(iii), 2.39(i)
6178	Joist hangers	
	Part 1: Joist hangers for building into masonry walls of domestic dwellings	2.81.1
*6209	Solvent cement for non-pressure thermoplastics pipe systems	2.32.4
6213	Guide to the selection of constructional sealants	2.125(iii)
6323	Seamless and welded steel tubes for automobile, mechanical and general engineering purposes	
	Part 2: Specific requirements for hot finished welded steel tubes	2.44.1, 2.68.1, 2.74.1
	Part 3: Specific requirements for hot finished seamless steel tubes	2.68.1
	Part 4: Specific requirements for cold finished seamless steel tubes	2.68.1
	Part 5: Specific requirements for electric resistance welded (including induction welded) steel tubes	2.68.1
	Part 6: Specific requirements for cold finished electric resistance welded (including induction welded) steel tubes	2.68.1
	Part 7: Specific requirements for submerged arc welded steel tubes	2.68.1

BS	TITLE	REFERENCE(S)
	Part 8: Specific requirements for longitudinally welded stainless steel tubes	2.74.1
6398	Bitumen damp-proof courses for masonry	2.127.1
6431	Ceramic floor and wall tiles	
	Part 1: Classification and marking, including definitions and characteristics	2.99.1, 2.99(i), 2.100.1
	*Part 2: Extruded ceramic tiles with a low water absorption (E≤ 3%) Group A1.	2.99.1, 2.99(i), 2.100.1
	Section 3.1: General products	2.99.1, 2.99(i), 2.100.1
	Section 3.2: Specific products (terre cuite, cotto, baldosin catalan)	2.99.1, 2.99(i), 2.100.1
	Section 4.1: General products	2.99.1, 2.99(i), 2.100.1
	Section 4.2: Specific products (terre cuite, cotto, baldosin catalan)	2.99.1, 2.99(i), 2.100.1
	Part 5: Extruded ceramic tiles with a water absorption of E > 10% Group A III	2.99.1, 2.99(i), 2.100.1
	*Part 6: Dust-pressed caramic tiles with a low water absorption (≤ 3%) Group B1	2.99.1, 2.99(i), 2.100.1
	*Part 7: Dust-pressed ceramic tiles with a water absorption of 3% E ≤ 6% Group B11a	2.99.1, 2.99(i), 2.100.1
	*Part 8: Dust-pressed ceramic tiles with a water absorption of 6% < E ≤ 10% Group B11b.	2.99.1, 2.99(i), 2.100.1
	*Part 9: Dust-pressed ceramic tiles with a water absorption of (E > 10%) Group B111	2.99.1, 2.99(i), 2.1001
6446	Manufacturer of glued structural components of timber and wood based panel products	6.19.2
6452	Beads for internal plastering and dry lining	
	Part 1: Galvanised steel beads	2.97.1
*6457	Reconstructed stone masonry units	2.112.2
*6510	Steel windows, sills, window boards and doors	2.90.1, 2.91.2
6515	Polyethylene damp-proof courses for masonry	2.127(i)
6566	Plywood	
	Part 1: Construction of panels and characteristics of plies including marking	2.83.1
	Part 2: Glossary of terms	2.83.1
	Part 3: Acceptance levels for post-manufacture batch testing including sampling	2.83.1
	Part 4: Tolerances on the dimensions of plywood panels	2.83.1
	Part 5: Moisture content	2.83.1
	Part 6: Limits of defects for the classification of plywood by appearance	2.83.1
	Part 7: Classification of resistance to fungal decay and wood borer attack	2.83.1
	Part 8: Bond performance of veneer plywood	2.83.1
*6572	Blue polyethylene pipes up to nominal size 63 for below ground use for potable water	2.36.1, 2.40.1
6576	Installation of chemical damp-proof courses	6.4.1
*6588	Portland pulverized-fuel ash cements	2.15.1
*6610	Pozzolanic pulverized fuel ash cement	2.15.1, 2.15(iii)
6683	Guide to installation and use of valves	2.49(ii)
6699	Ground granulated blastfurnace slag for use with Portland cement	2.13.1, 2.15.1
6717	Precast concrete paving blocks	
	*Part 1: Paving blocks	2.115.2

BS	TITLE	REFERENCE(S)
*6730	Black polyethylene pipes up to nominal size 63 for above ground use for cold potable water	2.36(ii)
6900	Raw, refined and boiled linseed oils for paints and varnishes	2.94.2
6920	Suitability of non-metallic products for use in contact with water intended for human consumption with regard to their effect on the quality of the water	
	Part 1: Specification	2.1(vi), 2.49.2
	Part 2: Methods of test	2.1(vi), 2.49.2
	Section 2.1: Samples for testing	2.1(vi), 2.49.2
	Section 2.2: Taste of water	2.1(vi), 2.49.2
	Subsection 2.2.1: General method of test	2.1(vi), 2.49.2
	Subsection 2.2.2: Method of testing tastes imparted to water by hoses	2.1(vi), 2.49.2
	Subsection 2.2.3: Method of testing tastes imparted to water by hoses for conveying water for food and drink preparation	2.1(vi), 2.49.2
	Section 2.3: Appearance of water	2.1(vi), 2.49.2
	Section 2.4: Growth of aquatic micro-organisms	2.1(vi), 2.49.2
	Section 2.5: The extraction of substances that may be of concern to public health	2.1(vi), 2.49.2
	Section 2.6: The extraction of metals	2.1(vi), 2.49.2
	Part 3: High temperature tests	2.1(vi), 2.49.2
*6925	Mastic asphalt for building and civil engineering (limestone aggregate)	2.101.1
6952	Exterior wood coating systems	
	Part 1: Guide to classification and selection	6.26(i)
7263	Precast concrete flags, kerbs, channels, edgings and quadrants	2.114.1, 2.115.1
	Part 1: Specification	
7331	Direct surfaced wood chipboard based on thermosetting resins	2.98.1
*7412	Plastics windows made from PVC-U extruded hollow profiles	2.90(i)
*7413	White PVC-U extruded hollow profiles with heat welded corner joints for plastics windows: materials type A.	2.90.1
*7414	White PVC-U extruded hollow profiles with heat welded corner joints for plastics windows: materials type B.	2.90.1
7475	Fusion welding of austenitic stainless steels	2.71(i)

* British Standards under which the BSI Certification Trade Mark is used. (See Clause 2.1).

APPENDIX III

List of British Standard Codes of Practice to which reference is made in the document

BS	TITLE	REFERENCE(S)
CP 144	Roof coverings	
	Part 3: Build-up bitumen felt. Metric units	2.103(i), 6.28.1, 6.30.1
	Part 4: Mastic asphalt. Metric units	2.103(i), 6.29.1
CP 204	In-situ floor finishes	
	Part 2: Metric Units	6.16.1
CP 312	Plastics pipework (thermoplastics material)	
	Part 1: General principles and choice of material	5.1(i)
	Part 2: Unplasticized PVC pipework for the conveyance of liquids under pressure	5.1(i)
	Part 3: Polyethylene pipes for the conveyance of liquids under pressure	5.1(i)
5228	Noise control on construction and open sites	
	Part 1: Basic information and procedures for noise control	1.AT.1
	Part 2: Guide to noise control legislation for construction and demolition, including road construction and maintenance	1.AT.1
5262	External renderings	6.17.1
5268	Structural use of timber	
	Part 2: Permissible stress design, materials and workmanship	2.84.1
	Part 3: Trussed rafter roofs	6.21.1
	Part 5: Preservative treatment of structural timber	2.84.3
5385	Wall and floor tiling	
	Part 1: Design and installation of internal ceramic wall tiling and mosaics in normal conditions	6.18.1
	Part 2: Design and installation of external ceramic wall tiling and mosaics (including terra cotta and faience tiles)	6.18.1
	Part 3: Design and installation of ceramic floor tiles and mosaics	6.15.1
	Part 4: Tiling and mosaics in specific conditions	6.18.1
	Part 5: Design and installation of terrazzo tile and slab, natural stone and composition block floorings	6.15.1
5390	Stone masonry	2.110(i)
5395	Stairs, ladders and walkways	
	Part 1: Design of straight stairs	2.76(ii)
	Part 2: Design of helical and spiral stairs	2.76(ii)
	Part 3: Design of industrial type stairs, permanent ladders and walkways	2.76(ii)
5449	Forced circulation hot water central heating systems for domestic premises	6.32(i)
5492	Internal plastering	6.12.4
5493	Protective coating of iron and steel structures against corrosion	6.26.1
5534	Slating and tiling	
	Part 1: Design	6.27.1
5589	Preservation of timber	2.84.2
5606	Guide to accuracy in building	6.34.1
5607	Safe use of explosives in the construction industry	1.19.3, 3.14.4
5628	Use of masonry	
	Part 3: Materials and components, design and workmanship	2.17(i), 2.20(i), 6.1.1, 6.1(i), 6.4.1

BS	TITLE	REFERENCE(S)
5837	Guide for trees in relation to construction	3.11.2, 3.11.4
5927	Guide for laying of asbestos-cement pipelines	5.1(i)
5930	Site investigations	1.AT.9(ii)
5955	Plastics pipework (thermoplastics materials)	
	Part 6: Installation of unplasticized PVC pipework for gravity drains and sewers	5.1(i)
5975	Falsework	4.17(i)
6031	Earthworks	3.1(i)
6093	Design of joints and jointing in building construction	6.AT.2
6150	Painting of buildings	2.94(i), 6.26.1
6164	Safety in tunnelling in the construction industry	3.1(i)
6180	Protective barriers in and about buildings	2.74.1, 2.74(iii), 2.77(iii)
6187	Demolition	3.AT.1
6262	Glazing for buildings	2.93(i), 6.25.1
6399	Loading for buildings	
	Part 1: Dead and imposed loads	2.74(i)
6657	Guide to prevention of inadvertent initiation of electro-explosive devices by radio-frequency radiation	3.14.3
6700	Design, installation, testing and maintenance of services supplying water for domestic use within buildings and their curtilages	6.32.1
6880	Low temperature hot water heating systems of output greater than 45kW	
	Part 1: Fundamental and design considerations	6.32.(i)
	Part 2: Selection of equipment	6.32.(i)
	Part 3: Installation, commissioning and maintenance	6.32(i)
7361	Cathodic protection	
	Part 1: Land and marine applications	5.14(iv)
7375	Distribution of electricity on construction and building sites	1.20(ii)
8004	Foundations	3.AT.1
8005	Sewerage	
	Part 1: Guide to new sewerage construction	5.1(i), 5.20(i), 7.5(i), 7.6(i)
8007	Design of concrete structures for retaining aqueous liquids	2.10(v), 2.15(v), 4.1(i), 4.6(i) 4.27(i), 7.13(i), 7.13(iii), 7.14(ii)
8010	Pipelines	5.1(i)
	Part 1: Pipelines on land: General	5.1(i)
	Section 2.1: Ductile iron	5.1(i)
	Section 2.3: Asbestos cement	5.1(i)
	Section 2.4: Prestressed concrete pressure pipelines	5.1(i)
	Section 2.5: Glass reinforced thermosetting plastics	5.1(i)
	Section 2.7: Precast concrete	5.1(i)
	Section 2.8: Steel for oil and gas	5.1(i), 5.11(i)
8102	Protection of structures against water from the ground	6.4.1
8110	Structural use of concrete	2.15(iii), 2.15(v),
	Part 1: Design and construction	2.16(ii), 4.1(i), 4.2(iv), 4.3(iv) 4.3(vi), 4.9(i), 4.15(ii), 4.29(i)
8203	Installation of sheet and tile flooring	6.15.1
8204	In-situ floorings	
	Part 2: Concrete wearing surfaces	4.30.1, 6.14.1, 6.14(i)
8215	Design and installation of damp-proof courses in masonry construction	6.4.1
8313	Accommodation of building services in ducts	2.44(i)

APPENDIX IV

List of British Standards Special Issues to which reference is made in the document

PD	TITLE	REFERENCE(S)
6472	Guide to specifying the quality of building mortars	2.20(i)

APPENDIX V

List of British Standards Drafts for Development to which reference is made in the document

DD	TITLE	REFERENCE(S)
140	Wall ties	
	Part 2: Recommendations for design of wall ties	2.106(i)
201	Suitability of metallic materials for use in contact with water intended for human consumption with regard to their effect on the quality of the water	2.1(vi), 2.49.2

APPENDIX VI

List of publications by the Water Services Association (WSA) and its predecessors to which reference is made in the document

NUMBER	TITLE	REFERENCE(S)

Occasional Technical Papers

| 2 | Operational Guidelines for the Protection of Drinking Water Supplies | 1.15.2, 1.15(i) |

Health and Safety

| 2 | Safe working in sewers and at sewage works | 1.16.1, 1.16(i) |

Others

	Sewerage Rehabilitation Manual	9. General Note 9.1(ii)
	Water Mains Rehabilitation Manual	9. General Note
	Principles of laying sewers	5.1(i)

APPENDIX VII

List of Water Industry specifications/Information and Guidance Notes to which reference is made in the document

Note: Water Industry specifications (WIs) have replaced Information and Guidance Notes (IGNs) and adopt the same numbering system - see 2.1(ii).

WIs/IGN	NUMBER	TITLE	REFERENCE(S)
IGN	4-08-01	Bedding and sidefill materials for buried pipelines	2.50(ii)
WIs	4-08-02	Specification for bedding and sidefill materials for buried pipelines	2.50.1
IGN	4-10-01	Bricks and mortar	2.20(ii), 2.105(ii)
IGN	4-11-01	Vitrified clay pipes and fittings	2.27(i)
IGN	4-12-01	Precast concrete pipes-unreinforced and reinforced, with flexible joints	2.28(iii)
IGN	4-12-03	Asbestos-cement pipes and fittings	2.33(i)
WIs	4-12-04	Specification for glassfibre reinforced cement (GRC) sewer linings	2.54.1
WIs	4-12-05	Specification for precast gunite sewer linings	2.54.1
WIs	4-12-06	Specification for precast and in-situ ferrocement	2.54.1
WIs	4-13-01	Specification for blastfurnace slag cement for in-situ lining of water mains	2.15.4
IGN	4-21-01	Ductile iron pipes and fittings	2.31(i)
WIs	4-22-01	Specification for compression fittings of copper and copper alloy for polyethylene pipes with outside diameters to BS 5556 (metric)	2.40.1
WIs	4-22-02	Specification for ferrules (tapping tees) and ferrule straps for underground use	2.40.1
IGN	4-23-01	Selection, installation, operation and maintenance of isolating and boundary valves used in water distribution systems	2.49(iii)
WIs	4-23-04	Specification for underground stop valves, including spherical valves, for potable water services for nominal sizes up to and including 63 and nominal pressures of 10 bar minimum and made principally of metal or thermoplastics	2.40.1
WIs	4-24-01	Specification for mechanical fittings and joints including flanges for PE pipes for the conveyance of cold potable water for the size range 90-1000 made of metal or plastics or a combination of both	2.36.4
IGN	4-31-01	Unplasticized PVC pipes and fittings	2.32(i), 5.8(iv)
WIs	4-31-02	Specification for plasticized PVC waterstops for use in construction and expansion joints in concrete water retaining structures	2.126.1
IGN	4-31-03	Guide to joint design and installation of PVC waterstops in water retaining structures	2.126(ii)
WIs	4-31-05	Specification for solid wall concentric external rib-reinforced uPVC sewer pipe	2.32.4
WIs	4-31-06	Specification for blue, unplasticized PVC pressure pipes, integral joints and post-formed bends for cold potable water (underground use)	2.32.1, 2.32(iii)
WIs	4-31-07	Specification for unplasticized PVC pressure fittings and assemblies for cold potable water (underground use).	2.32.1

WIs/IGN	NUMBER	TITLE	REFERENCE(S)
WIs	4-31-08	Specification for molecular oriented polyvinyl chloride (MOPVC) pressure pipes for underground use	2.32.1
WIs	4-32-03	Specification for blue polyethylene (PE) pressure pipe for cold potable water (nominal sizes 90 to 1000 for underground or protected use)	2.36.2
WIs	4-32-04	Specification for polyethylene socket and spigot fittings, saddles and drawn bends, for use with cold potable water PE pressure pipes	2.36.3
WIs	4-32-05	Specification for polyethylene (PE) pipes for sewer linings (non-pressure applications)	2.54.1
WIs	4-32-06	Specification for PE electrofusion couplers and fittings for cold water supply for nominal sizes up to and including 180	2.36.3
WIs	4-32-08	Specification for site fusion jointing of MDPE pipe and fittings	5.8.2
WIs	4-32-09	Specification for black polyethylene pressure pipes for potable water above ground or sewerage (nominal sizes 90 to 1000)	2.36.2
WIs	4-32-10	Specification for non-circular polyethylene sewer linings	2.54.1
WIs	4-32-11	Specification for end load resistant mechanical joints and compression fittings made principally of thermoplastics for use with polyethylene pipes of nominal size $\leq$63 with outside diameters to BS 5556 (metric)	2.40.1
WIs	4-32-13	Specification for blue higher performance polyethylene HPPE/PE 100, pressure pipes, nominal size 90 to 1000, for underground or protected use for the conveyance of water intended for human consumption	2.36.2
WIs	4-33-01	Specification for polypropylene encapsulated steps for use in manholes and access chambers	2.58.1
IGN	4-34-01	GRP pipes and fittings	2.34(i)
WIs	4-34-02	Specification for glassfibre reinforced plastics (GRP) sewer linings	2.54.1
WIs	4-34-04	Specification for polyester insituform sewer linings	2.54.1
WIs	4-34-05	Specification for polyester resin concrete (PRC) sewer linings	2.54.1
WIs	4-37-01	Specification for boundary boxes for the metering and control of domestic and small industrial water services	2.62.1, 2.62.2
IGN	4-40-01	Selection, properties, storage and installation requirements for elastomeric seals and sealing rings	2.46(i)
IGN	4-40-02 (EU14-001)	Guidance for the selection properties and use of elastomeric seals and sealing components (English and French language)	2.46(ii)
IGN	4-50-01	Operational guidelines for the loose polyethylene sleevings of underground iron mains	2.26(ii)
IGN	4-50-02	Operational guidelines for the transportation, handling and laying of ductile iron pipes with factory applied polyethylene sleeving	2.26(iii)
IGN	4-51-01	External zinc coating of ductile iron pipe	2.31(ii)
WIs	4-52-01	Specification for polymeric anti-corrosion (barrier) coatings	2.31(iii)

WIs/IGN	NUMBER	TITLE	REFERENCE(S)
IGN	4-52-02	The use of polymeric anti-corrosion (barrier) coatings	2.31(iii)
WIs	4-60-01	Specification for building and construction joints sealants	2.125.1
IGN	5-01-01	The United Kingdom Water Fitting Byelaws Scheme	2.40(iii)
IGN	5-01-02	Requirements for the testing of non-metallic products for use in contact with potable water	2.1(vi), 2.49.2

Copies of these documents can be obtained from WRc Publications, P O Box 16, Marlow, Bucks, SL7 2HD, Tel (0491) 571531, Fax: (0491) 579094

IGN   4-52-02   The use of polymeric anti-corrosion (barrier) coatings

APPENDIX VIII

List of Construction Industry Research and Information Association (CIRIA) publications to which reference is made in the document

NUMBER	TITLE	REFERENCE(S)
R44	Medical Code of Practice for Work in Compressed Air, 3rd Edition 1982 (Reprinted with amendments 1992)	1.17.1, 1.17(ii), 3.6.4
R59	Building Sands: availability, usage and compliance with specification requirements	2.12(i)
R67	Tables of minimum striking times for soffit and vertical formwork	4.19(i)
R73	Formwork striking times - methods of assessment	4.19(i)
R97	Trenching Practice	3.1(i)
TN71	A guide to the use of grass in hydraulic engineering practice	2.6(v)
TN75	Load tests on fixings in concrete	2.77(iv)
TN95	Proprietary trench support systems	3.1(i)
TN104	Precast concrete tunnel linings - review of current test procedures	2.63(ii)
TN128	Civil engineering sealants in wet conditions	2.125(v)
TN137	Selection and use of fixings in concrete and masonry - An update to CIRIA Guide 4	2.77(ii)
TN144	Performance of sealant concrete joints in wet conditions. Volume 1 - Results of a laboratory testing programme. Main results and discussion	2.125(v)
SP25	Site investigation manual	1.AT.9(ii)

APPENDIX IX

List of statutory references in the document.

TITLE	REFERENCE(S)
Explosives Acts 1875 and 1923	1.19(i)
Petroleum (Consolidation) Act 1928	1.19(i)
Petroleum Spirit (Motor Vehicles etc.) Regulations 1929	1.19(i)
Public Health Act 1936	1.AT.13
Work in Compressed Air Special Regulations 1958	1.17(i)
Construction (General Provisions) Regulations 1961 (SI 1961/1580)	1.19(i), 1.AT.3, 2.84(i)
Factories Act 1961	1.AT.8
Construction (Health and Welfare) Regulations 1966	1.AT.8
Construction (Working Places) Regulations 1966 (SI 1966/94)	1.AT.7
Highly Flammable Liquids and Liquefied Petroleum Gases Regulations 1972	1.19(i)
Control of Pollution Act 1974 (SI 1992/84)	1.AT.1
Health and Safety and Work etc. Act 1974	1.AT.1
Construction (Health and Welfare) (Amended) Regulations 1974	1.AT.8
Salmon and Fresh Water Fisheries Act 1975	1.14(ii)
Fire Certificates (Special Premises) Regulations 1976 (SI 1976/2003)	1.AT.12
Health and Safety (First Aid) Regulations 1981 (SI 1981/917)	1.AT.5
Wildlife and Countryside Act 1981	2.6(vi)
Control of Noise (Codes of Practice for Construction and Open sites) Order 1984	1.AT.1
Construction (Metrication) Regulations 1984 (SI 1984/1593)	1.AT.3, 1.AT.7, 2.84(i)
Water Supply (Water Quality) Regulations 1989	2.1(v)
Council Directive on the approximation of laws, regulations and administrative provisions of the Member States relating to construction products (89/106/EEC)	Foreword, Product Specifications and Levels of attestation, 2.1.3, 2.1(vii)
Council Directive on the procurement procedures of entities in the water, energy, transport and telecommunications sectors (90/531/EEC)	2.1(vii)
Environmental Protection Act 1990	3.1(viii)
New Roads and Street Works Act 1991	Foreword, 1.11(vi), 1.12.1, 1.AT.4, 3 General Note
Water Industry Act 1991	1.1.3, 1.7(ii)
Water Resources Act 1991	1.14(iii)
Land Drainage Act 1991	1.14(iii)
Control of Explosives Regulations 1991	1.19(i)
Street Works Regulations 1992	3 General Note
Specifications for the Reinstatement of Openings in Highways	3.12, 3.9(i)

APPENDIX X

List of Miscellaneous Publications to which reference is made in the document.

NUMBER	TITLE	REFERENCE(S)
	A Guide to Pipe Jacking Design - Pipe jacking Association	5.25(ii)
Digest 330	Alkali - silica Reaction - Building Research Establishment	2.10(iii), 2.15(vi), 4.3(v)
TR 30	Alkali - silica Reaction - Minimising the Risk of Damage to Concrete-Concrete Society	2.10(iii), 2.15(vi), 4.3(v)
	ASTM D3595 - American Society for Testing Materials	2.124.5
	Design of normal concrete mixes - Department of the Environment (BRE Report, BR 106)	4.3(vii)
	Guide to practice in corrosion control - No. 9 Cathodic Protection - National Corrosion Service of the National Physical Laboratory.	5.14(iv)
Digest 276	Hardcore - Building Research Establishment	2.116(i)
	Model Consultative Procedure for Pipeline Construction Involving Deep Excavation - British Gas/WSA/WCA	1.11(ii)
Advice Note TD/21/85	Portable Traffic Signals at Roadworks on Single Carriageway Roads - Department of Transport	1.12.1
	Regulations for Electrical Installations, 16th Edition - Institution of Electrical Engineers	1.20.1, 1.20(i), 1.20(ii) 6.AT.1
Advice Note 13/81	Requirements for the Installation of Traffic Signals and Associated Control Equipment - Department of Transport	1.12.1
	Safety at Street Works and Road Works - HMSO	1.12.1, 1.AT.4
	Specification for Highway Works - Department of Transport	2.117.2, 2.124.1, 3.13(i) 8. General Note
	Specification for Piling: Contract Documentation and Measurement - Institution of Civil Engineers	3. AT.2
	Statement of the Committee on Chemicals and Materials of Construction for Use in Public Water Supply and Swimming Pools - Department of the Environment	2.1(v)
	The Water Industry's Duty under the Health and Safety at Work etc. Act to Contractors Employed by the Industry - National Joint Health and Safety Committee Employers' side	1.AT.15
Advice Note TD/12/81	Traffic signals on high speed roads - Department of Transport	1.12.1
	Traffic Signs Manual - Department of Transport	1.12.1
	Water Fittings and Materials Directory - WRc	2.1(v)

APPENDIX XI

DETAILS OF PROBLEM/COMPLAINT UPON QUALITY ASSURED PRODUCTS

1. Name of complainant ....

2. The product and specification reference ....

    ....

3. Name of manufacturer ....

4. Details of the product i.e. size, type, class, date of manufacture (if known), batch number (if known) etc.

    ....

    ....

    ....

5. How many items appear unsatisfactory? ....

6. How many items were ordered? ....

7. Were quality assured products ordered?   YES/NO

8. Were all the products delivered, marked with a mark of conformity?   YES/NO

9. Date the products were delivered? ....

10. When was the problem delivered? ....

11. Were the products supplied by: the manufacturer/a merchant ....

12. With which clauses of the specification do the products appear not to comply:

    Nos. ....

13. Details of problem/complaint ....

    ....

    ....

14. Has the manufacturer been advised of the problem?   YES/NO

15. If yes to 14 what was the response? ....

    ....

16. If no to 14, do you wish us to reveal to the manufacturer that you are the complainant?   YES/NO

17. Have the products all be installed?   YES/NO

18. Do you wish the products to be examined on Site by a certification body representative?   YES/NO

19. If yes to 18 please give details of Site location and name of contact. ....
    (We shall arrange a mutually convenient date to visit the site).

INDEX TO SPECIFICATION